NASM CPT Study Guide 2024-2025

Review Book with 360 Practice Questions and Answer Explanations for the Certified Personal Trainer Exam

Contents

Free Video Offer!

Thank you for purchasing from Hanley Test Preparation! We're honored to help you prepare for your exam. To show our appreciation, we're offering an Exclusive Test Tips Video.

This video includes multiple strategies that will make you successful on your big exam.

All we ask is that you email us your feedback and describe your experience with our product. Amazing, awful, or just so-so. We want to hear what you have to say!

To get your FREE VIDEO, just send us an email at bonusvideo@hanleytestprep.com with **Free Video** in the subject line and the following information in the body of the email:

- The name of the product you purchased
- Your product rating on a scale of 1-5, with 5 being the highest rating.
- Your feedback about the product.

If you have any questions or concerns, please don't hesitate to contact us at support@hanleytestprep.com

Thanks again!

Introduction

To be an effective personal trainer, there are many things a person needs to know. A personal trainer must understand technique, movement, health, anatomy, physiology, and behavior. They need to be effective communicators, professionals, and brand creators. All of these skills create a personal trainer who makes a positive impact on those working to overcome their challenges. A lot of knowledge and skill goes into being the support your clients need. All of these essentials can seem overwhelming.

Fortunately, the National Association of Sports Medicine Certification for Personal Trainers (NASM CPT) provides you not only with the necessary information but also with the ability to demonstrate that you are capable. NASM is known for its courses that prepare fitness professionals to enter the workforce, advance their careers, and help prove their knowledge. Compared to other programs, the NASM CPT is one of the best options, as it is accredited, contains high-quality content, is cost-effective, and the exam has the least amount of questions.

The NASM CPT is well-known and highly valued in the industry. With a reputation for teaching trainers a wide variety of skills, a trainer with this certification will stand out from others who do not have this rigorous training. Simply having this certification will open up new opportunities, as it will be proof of your abilities and knowledge. This demand for NASM-certified trainers can lead to a higher pay rate, as clients are willing to pay more for a trainer they can trust.

This exam study guide has everything you need to ace the 2024-2025 NASM CPT, complete with practice exams and answer keys with explanations. To do well in this exam, you need to be both mentally and physically prepared. The practice exams will help students get a feel for the exam, while the answer keys will allow them to review their knowledge and understand areas for improvement. This book will help you feel uniquely prepared to succeed. Students who use this book as a resource will be prepared for the exam and their careers.

The NASM CPT has a relatively high pass rate, at 74%. The difference between those who pass and those who fail is their level of preparedness. It can take 4-12 weeks for a student to prepare for the exam using one of the study guides. This wide range demonstrates that the student is the best judge of their readiness and abilities. Depending on your needs, you may be inclined to breeze through or take your time exploring and reviewing topics.

However, knowing these statistics does not ease all test-taking anxiety, as 26% of students will not pass the exam. Many students become overwhelmed by the sheer volume of information they need to learn to pass. The stress and anxiety can become crippling to the point that they avoid studying at all.

Other students don't necessarily feel the stress that comes from exams but are not sure how to study. Not knowing what questions are in the exam or which topics to devote their time to can cause them to be unprepared for the test. Nothing is more frustrating than spending time carefully studying a topic, only to realize the exam focuses on something entirely different.

Many students simply lack the motivation to study. Without a sense of structure and organization, they find themselves drifting into procrastination, only to panic when they realize they aren't ready for the exam. Students then attempt to cram all their studying into a short period. This last-minute study session, with none of the tools necessary for success, is unlikely to end in a pass result.

The solutions to all these problems are found in this book. Unlike other study resources, this book goes beyond a simple review, offering practical advice on how to combat exam stress and anxiety. The Awareness, Combat, and Excel (ACE) method helps students be aware of their anxieties and overcome them. For students who feel as though stress is keeping them from success, this method will help them get back on track.

This study guide also provides the information necessary to pass the exam. Unlike other study resources, this guide doesn't just tell you whether you got the answer correct. It also provides you with an explanation that will deepen your understanding and help you make connections for an exam that focuses heavily on the practical application.

For students who lack the motivation to study, this guide lays out the information in an easy-to-follow structure. Often, a lack of motivation comes from feeling a disconnect between what you want to achieve (a pass score) and the tools you have available (an ineffective study guide). With a study guide that provides organized topics, students who face that frustration will be able to feel that their tools are more than capable of handling the task.

With this book, you will be able to pursue the dream of being the best personal trainer you can be. There is a need for people who can effectively help others become healthy and happy. Sharing in the journey is one of the unique privileges of being a personal trainer. As a personal trainer, you will take an active role in helping others achieve their dreams. You become their support as they work through nutritional, physical, and lifestyle changes. I promise that this book will help you pass the NASM CPT and be able to make a positive difference in the lives of people who need you.

It can be difficult to put forth the work to pursue your dreams. But the sooner you get started, the sooner you will be able to make those dreams a reality. Studying for the exam using this study guide is the first step on the journey. If you want to begin the journey to being a great personal trainer, all you need to do is begin with this first step.

Chapter One: The ACE Method

Most students are only too familiar with test anxiety. This kind of anxiety involves feelings of dread, hopelessness, and defeat. It even involves the physical responses that come from anxiety, like an elevated heart rate, sweating, and nausea. When students feel this anxiety about an exam, they have distorted views of reality. They perceive the exam as being extremely important and impossibly difficult, with little chance of success. It's a prevalent concern, with anywhere from 20 to 40% of students reporting test-related anxiety.

However, understanding the effects of test anxiety is essential to understand why it needs to be addressed and taken seriously. Test anxiety cannot be dismissed as simply being a bit nervous before a test. It has an impact on both the student's performance in the exam and on their overall well-being.

Yet, a large majority of students who feel test anxiety do not get any form of assistance. Many believe that this type of anxiety is common, and best solved by ignoring it or toughing it out. However, the solution to test anxiety is not to ignore it. Excessive fear can make it difficult to concentrate. Negative self-evaluation can become a self-fulfilling prophecy. The higher the test anxiety, the worse students perform in an exam. If a student wants to set themselves up for success, the solution is not to ignore test anxiety and hope it goes away.

The way to set yourself up for success is to use a method that helps you to be **aware** of your fears, **combat** them, and **excel** during the exam. This is the ACE method, a strategy that helps students overcome self-doubt and anxiety and excel in preparing and taking tests. These three simple steps will help you on the path to success.

Awareness

Awareness means that you acknowledge what you are feeling. The first step to making any change is identifying where you are in the present, so you know how to move forward. When it comes to taking tests, many students find the overwhelming issue to acknowledge is test anxiety. While a small amount of anxiety can help a student stay motivated and engaged, when taken to an extreme, anxiety will cause students to perform poorly in exams.

Therefore, a student should not simply address the feelings, but the extent to which they feel them. In the same way that medical professionals may ask a patient to rate their pain on a scale from one to ten, you can rate your anxiety and stress levels so you can better assess if your anxiety is helping or hindering.

According to the Anxiety and Depression Association of America, symptoms of test anxiety can be physical, behavioral, cognitive, and emotional. As you evaluate your test anxiety, notice what symptoms you are experiencing. If it is physical, you may experience sweating, nausea, or fainting, as if you were coming down with a fever. If it is behavioral or cognitive, you may begin avoiding test scenarios by refusing to study, skipping class, or even considering dropping out of the program. If it is emotional, you may feel negative emotions like hopelessness, anger, dread, or fear (Cherry, Kendra, 2023).

Although these symptoms may seem like an overreaction to a test, there are legitimate reasons to feel this way. If students connect their self-worth to their success, it may feel as though failure is not an option. The only way they feel good about themselves is to succeed, leading them to fear failure to an extreme level. Other times, students get stuck in a loop of doing poorly in tests. Because they performed poorly on the last test, they fear doing poorly on future tests. Because they let themselves become distracted by their fear, they continue to perform poorly in exams, until it seems as though success is not possible. There are many unique reasons to be nervous about tests. As you become more aware of your feelings about taking tests, consider what the causes of your test anxiety may be.

Combat

Once you have a full understanding of your anxieties, you know your enemy. You know how the degree to which your anxiety is creating challenges for you, the symptoms you experience, and the reasons for your fears. Now, you can combat your anxiety.

In the same way that your symptoms can be broken up into physical, behavioral/cognitive, and emotional, your solutions can be grouped in the same way.

Dealing with the physical solutions is a great way to feel purposeful and hands-on about your test preparation. Many students try to pull all-nighters before a test as they study, fuel themselves with caffeine, or refuse to take breaks as they pursue their goals. However, all of these habits will increase test anxiety. A good night's sleep, staying away from energy drinks, and frequent breaks will help you feel physically relaxed enough to succeed in the exam.

These may seem like overly simple solutions, but your mind and body need the opportunity to reset to make new neural pathways. Retaining information will be much easier if you have a good foundation of healthy habits to build on top of. Many students also find meditative practices to be an effective way to help them feel more capable in their studies. If you are struggling with test anxiety, try some deep breaths, muscle relaxation, or mindfulness.

Remember that your breaks are as important as your studies. While mindlessly scrolling social media may seem like a good way to disconnect, it does not make your breaks especially meaningful. Use your breaks to connect with others, spend time in nature, or otherwise do something genuinely enjoyable for you.

Cognitive strategies revolve around helping you create the behaviors necessary to succeed. Often, fear of testing causes students to miss out on the things that will help them reach their goals. By practicing taking tests, students can create the habit of showing up for the things that scare them. For instance, students can take practice tests or study in places that are similar to the environment they are taking the test in.

One helpful strategy is positive visualization. This is where students imagine what success would look like, with as many details as possible. If a student imagines themselves walking into a test center, putting pencil to paper, and feeling confident in their answers, then they are practicing success. When anxiety tends to force us to focus on the worst possible scenario, it can be helpful to envision the best possible scenario.

The emotional solutions help you directly take on the anxiety and fear that you are experiencing. One of the most straightforward ways to do this is by questioning your fears. Negative emotions tend to distort your version of reality. If you're thinking in absolutes, like "always," "never," or "everybody," that's a pretty good sign that you are being too extreme in your views. Ask yourself what the worst and best-case scenario is. Even if it's not ideal, can you live with the consequences if things don't go right?

Thinking positively can also help you brush off the anxiety and stress you may be feeling. Remind yourself why you are taking the exam and what you want to accomplish as a personal trainer. Remind yourself of your many talents and abilities outside of the results of a test. Sometimes negative thoughts can be persistent. The best way to get rid of them is to replace them with something else.

There are occasions when your best efforts to tackle this anxiety don't seem to be working. In that case, it may be time to call on the assistance of someone who can help. Sometimes it is enough to ask friends and family for their empathy and advice. Other times, students will need to involve a professional to help them sort through their feelings. Either way, you are not alone in the battle against your anxiety.

If you want to combat your test anxiety, it might be easiest to view it as a step-by-step process. Whenever you are preparing to study, try these tricks:

1. Begin a study session by reminding yourself of your overarching goal. While passing the test may be the immediate goal, your long-term goal involves the reason why you want to be a personal trainer. Let that goal guide you forward by beginning every study session with that in mind.

2. Set up your study station to be similar to the testing area. As you succeed in your studies, you will be able to visualize yourself succeeding in the exam.

3. Study for no more than an hour before taking a fifteen to twenty-minute break. During this break time, do something you genuinely enjoy doing. Get a snack, talk to a friend, or spend some time out of doors.

4. Return to your studies, repeating the process. Never let these study sessions go on during times that you should be sleeping, as sleep will prepare you for the test ahead.

On your exam day:

1. Get to bed at a reasonable time so that you can wake up early in the morning. If you are concerned about sleeping past your alarm, set multiple alarms or arrange to have someone call you to make sure you are up. This will allow you to start your day off with a win.
2. Be at the exam location early. If your exam is at a physical location, this will allow you to feel comfortable in the space before the exam begins. If it is an online test, this will allow you to sort out any technical issues ahead of time.
3. Begin the test with what you know. There is no need to answer all questions linearly. Answering questions you feel most confident at in the beginning will let you begin the test with confidence.
4. When you begin to feel overwhelmed, take a few deep breaths. Remind yourself that, even if this test does not go well, you can still pursue your dreams.

While you may still feel some anxiety, understanding that you can fight your fears will help you overcome them. These simple solutions, when followed, will help you relieve the pressure you have put on yourself to succeed, allowing you to excel.

Test anxiety is common. If you find yourself experiencing the symptoms of anxiety, you are not alone. However, there is no reason to try to power through this fear when there is a systematic approach to gaining awareness of your anxiety, combating these negative symptoms, and excelling.

As you approach the remainder of this study guide, remember that you have the power over your own emotions. You can identify where these emotions are coming from, what issues you are struggling with, and how serious your anxiety is. You are also equipped to combat your anxiety in several areas. Whether it is physical, cognitive, or emotional, you have a plan to overcome your symptoms.

With these tools at your disposal, you not only take the exam but excel at it. Creating confidence in your success is one of the most important aspects of studying. While the content is essential, having an ACE mindset allows you to put that knowledge into practice and succeed.

Excel

Excelling goes beyond simply achieving good marks in an exam. By using the ACE method, you change the way you engage with study materials. You make a shift from fear to confidence, changing the trajectory of your academic journey. You gain newfound self-assurance in your ability to do difficult things. This applies to studying for and taking the certification exam, but it goes well beyond that. Your confidence will also make you a better personal trainer in the future, as you prove to yourself and to clients that you can take on a challenge.

Chapter Summary

- Test anxiety is common among students.
- Test anxiety distorts student perception, affecting exam performance and student well-being.
- Awareness involves assessing anxiety, identifying the symptoms, and understanding its root cause.
- Combat involves addressing physical, cognitive/behavioral, and emotional symptoms with the appropriate solutions.
- Excelling goes beyond passing the test; it allows you to face all challenging circumstances with confidence.
- Put together, Aware, Combat and Excel create the ACE method, which helps students overcome their test anxiety.

In the next section, you will explore topics on basic and applied sciences and nutritional concepts. This information will be vital to success in the exam. It includes information on many different systems within the body, including muscular, skeletal, nervous, cardiorespiratory, endocrine, and digestive systems. Following an overview of the body, this section will discuss the science of human movement, metabolism, bioenergetics, nutrition, and supplementation. Although there is a lot of information to cover, this section will be the core of your scientific understanding of the human body. As you approach this upcoming section, remember to apply the skills learned in the ACE method to keep your study productive.

Chapter Two: Basic and Applied Sciences and Nutritional Concepts

The human body has been carefully organized and categorized into eleven different systems: the integumentary system, the skeletal system, the muscular system, the nervous system, the endocrine system, the cardiovascular system, the lymphatic system, the respiratory system, the digestive system, the urinary system, and the reproductive system. Not only are each of these systems a collection of organs working together to accomplish the purpose of the system, but each organ system works to accomplish its purpose within the human body.

Understanding the function of these organ systems is essential to understanding how to care for the human body. Each system needs to be in good order to maintain health. As a physical trainer, you need to know not only the function of these systems but also the impact of training on the body. If a personal trainer were to overlook this essential information, they would be unable to make well-informed decisions on the best training program for their clients.

For physical trainers, the organ systems of interest include the nervous, muscular, skeletal, cardiorespiratory, endocrine, and digestive systems. Although all systems work in conjunction with each other, these are the systems that are directly impacted by training.

The Nervous, Muscular, And Skeletal Systems

Human movement comes from the joint effort of the nervous, muscular, and skeletal systems. This collaboration of systems needs to be closely studied and understood. An issue with one of these systems will not only be detrimental to the others but will also impair movement and mobility. These systems are perhaps the most important to a physical trainer, as maintaining and strengthening this movement system is the main role of a physical trainer.

The Nervous System

The importance of the nervous system cannot be overemphasized. It controls, regulates, and communicates throughout the entire body. It creates all movement, including the ability to see, breathe, and think.

This entire system is made up of neurons, the cells that send electrical signals throughout your body. These neurons form the central nervous system, made up of the brain and spinal cord, and the peripheral nervous system, made up of the nerves that branch off the spinal cord and extend throughout the body. The peripheral nervous system contains two smaller systems.

1. **The somatic nervous system**, which controls voluntary muscle movement and the transmission of sensory information to the central nervous system.

2. **The autonomic nervous system**, which is responsible for automatic, involuntary functions, like breathing or keeping the heart beating.

Sensory and Motor Systems

The sensory system contains nerves that are responsible for communicating to the rest of the body when changes occur inside or outside the body. All sensory input that is gained from monitoring conditions is then sent to the brain, allowing us to see, hear, smell, touch, and taste. We don't have control over these sensory receptors. Their only job is to report the sensations. They are also known as afferents because they take information from outside and bring it in.

The motor system nerves are responsible for our movement. Rather than being afferent, bringing information into the brain, motor nerves are efferent and responsible for carrying electronic impulses outward. They carry signals to the muscles, helping them expand and contract with every movement.

Photoreceptors and Mechanoreceptors

These are two of the most important sensory receptors. Photoreceptors are the sensory cells in the retina that sense light. They include both rods, which allow people to see in dim lighting, and cones, which allow us to see color in bright lighting. This distinction explains why people see in shades of gray when it is too dark for the cones to function.

Mechanoreceptors are the cells throughout the body that respond to physical sensations, like pressure and vibration. They allow a person to feel touch, be aware of the position of their body, hear through sound vibrations, and control muscles. Both photoreceptors and mechanoreceptors receive information that allows us to perceive and respond to stimuli.

The Structure of the Nervous System

The nervous system has the key structure in place by birth. However, it continues to mature and develop throughout childhood, adolescence, and early adulthood. As the system develops, it grows new neural connections and refines motor skills.

Motor skills are developed during three main stages.

1. **The first two years of life**, the nervous system creates gross motor skills involving whole-body movements like crawling, standing, and walking.
2. **From two to seven years**, children learn fine motor skills, which involve precise movements, like using a pencil, scissors, or utensils.
3. **After seven years**, people begin to learn advanced motor skills, or

movements that are particular to a certain skill, like catching a baseball, dancing the foxtrot, or rock climbing.

To function and develop, the nervous system needs many different electrolytes. The main electrolytes are sodium, potassium, magnesium, and water.

- **Sodium** initiates the electrical signals, changes the electrical charge of a neuron, moves electrical signals along more rapidly, and restores the resting state. In short, sodium helps send the electrical signals necessary for the nervous system to function.
- **Potassium** restores the resting state, maintains the electrical balance, and acts as a calming agent within the nervous system. Essentially, this electrolyte helps the nerves send their messages properly.
- **Magnesium** regulates nerve function, assists in the interactions between the nervous and muscular systems, helps release neurotransmitters, promotes calmness, maintains healthy nerves, and regulates the creation and destruction of neural pathways. This electrolyte encompasses many different areas of neurological health.
- **Water** is essential throughout the body. In the case of the nervous system, water hydrates, transports, and regulates, in a similar fashion to its role throughout the rest of the body.

The nervous system is one of the most essential systems in the body. Without it, the human body would not be capable of sensation, movement, or even cognitive processes. It is a complex system, made up of neurons that create the central and peripheral nervous system. It is responsible for both voluntary and involuntary action, as well as the ability to sense internal and external stimuli.

This system builds and becomes capable of more complex movement over time. And this entire complex system relies on electrolytes to function properly. With all these complex processes, the nervous system is responsible for much of human movement.

The Skeletal System

The skeletal system is also very important for movement. It is responsible for supporting the body, facilitating movement, protecting internal organs, producing blood cells, and storing and releasing fat. It consists of bones, cartilage, ligaments, and tendons.

The skeletal system can be divided into two categories: the axial skeleton and the appendicular skeleton.

1. **The axial skeleton** is made up of the bones that run along the body's central axis. It includes the skull bone, which includes eight cranial bones, fourteen facial bones, six auditory ossicles, and the hyoid bone; the thoracic cage bone, which includes the breastbone and twenty-four ribs; and the vertebral column bone, which includes twenty-four vertebrae bones, the sacrum bone, and the coccyx bone.
2. **The appendicular skeleton** includes the pelvic girdle, upper limbs, lower limbs, and shoulder girdle.

In sum, the human body contains 206 bones, each of which is essential for movement. They provide the basic structure for the body, with tendons connecting bone to muscle, which allows the body to move. Some bones serve only as a support for the muscle, while others work with the muscle, creating a lever effect.

There are four main types of bones: long, short, flat, and irregular.

1. **Long bones** have greater length than width, and are used to support weight and facilitate movement, like the tibia bone.
2. **Short bones** have an equal length to width, and are used for stability and movement, like the carpal and tarsal bones.
3. **Flat bones** are flattened and shield-like, used to protest inner organs, like the ribs.
4. **Irregular bones** are those that don't fit into the other categories, like the vertebrae of the spine. Because irregular bones are so diverse, they perform a variety of functions.

Bones grow over time, in different ways throughout life. In childhood and adolescence, bones grow in both length and width. This is also the time in which many bones fuse together. Humans are born with 300 bones, but by adulthood, some of these bones will join to become one. Although bones stop this growth process in adulthood, after growth plates have closed, the bones will continue to repair and maintain themselves.

Bone growth and repair is done through three types of cells.

1. **Osteoblasts**, which form the bone, producing proteins needed to form new bone tissue.
2. **Osteoclasts**, which reabsorb old and damaged bone tissue.
3. **Osteocytes** monitor and coordinate bone growth and repair by sensing changes in the forces at play on the bone.

Together, these three cells maintain a healthy skeletal system throughout life.

The Vertebral Column

One of the most important areas for physical therapists to understand is the vertebral column, which is responsible for supporting much of the movement in the body. There are five distinct sections within the vertebral column, each with its own function.

1. **The cervical region** is made up of the first seven vertebrae, located in the neck. They are solely responsible for the movement of the head. They support the weight of the head and allow it to nod, tilt, and rotate.
2. **The thoracic region** is made up of twelve vertebrae located in the upper and middle back. They provide the necessary support for the ribcage and are vital for the protection of the heart and lungs. The small amount of movement that these vertebrae allow gives the lungs room to expand.
3. **The lumbar region** is made up of five vertebrae in the lower back. As the largest of the spinal bones, they carry most of the weight of the body. They are essential for providing stability during movement.
4. **The sacral region** is made of the five fused vertebrae that form the sacrum bone. This bone stabilizes the pelvis, connecting it to the vertebral column and attaching it to other muscles and ligaments. It works in conjunction with the hip bones.
5. **The coccygeal region** is made up of the several fused vertebrae that make up the coccyx bone. It has extremely limited mobility, with less importance to movement and support than the other regions of the vertebral column. However, it does create an attachment point for muscles and supports a seated position.

A very important part of the spinal column is the intervertebral discs. Between each vertebra sits a cushion of cartilage, without which the spine would cease to function correctly. They absorb shock that would otherwise overwhelm the spine. There are many instances in which the spine needs to compress to deal with impact forces, including movements like jumping, walking, or carrying a load. These discs also allow for more flexible movement than the rigid spine is capable of, allowing it to bend and twist. Importantly, the discs create space between each vertebrae. Not only does that reduce grinding between bones, but it also creates space for the spinal nerves. Without it, the spine would be nothing more than a painful collection of pinched nerves.

Like intervertebral discs, joints play an important part in facilitating movement at places where two bones meet. These joints can be formed with fibrous connective tissue (which allows for very little movement between the bones), cartilage (which allows for limited movement), or a synovial cavity (which allows for a greater range of movement due to the presence of synovial liquid, which lubricates the joint). Based on the amount of movement, joints can be classified as synarthroses (immovable), amphiarthroses (slightly moveable), and diarthroses (freely moveable).

The Synovial Joint

There are six different types of synovial joints, which explain the different ranges of motion possible.

1. **Hinge joints** have a rounded bone ending that fits into a curved bone ending, allowing for one movement. An example of this kind of joint is found at the elbow, where it allows the elbow to bend and straighten in one direction (flexion).
2. **Ball-and-socket joints** fit together when one bone has a ball-shaped ending and the other is shaped like a cup, allowing for movement in multiple directions. An example of this joint is found at the shoulder, allowing flexion (bending), extension, abduction (moving away from the body), adduction (moving toward the body), and rotation.
3. **Pivot joints** work when a rounded or pointed bone ending fits inside a bone end that is shaped like a sleeve, allowing for only rotational

movement. For instance, the joint between vertebrae in your neck allows you to shake your head.

4. **Ellipsoid joints** have an oval-shaped bone ending that fits into an elliptical bone ending, allowing flexion, extension, abduction, adduction (moving toward the body), and circumduction (a circular movement). An example of this type of joint is found in the wrist.

5. **Saddle joints** are created when two saddle-shaped bones come together, allowing for the same movements as ellipsoid joints. An example of this is found in the thumb joint.

6. **Gliding joints** have flat surfaces, allowing them to glide across each other in multiple directions. The carpals and tarsals in the wrist and ankle are examples of gliding joints.

There are two ways to describe the movement of these joints.

1. **Osteokinematics**, which describes the visible movements of the bones at the joints. These movements are easy to see and identify.

2. **Arthrokinematics**, which describes the movements that take place inside the joint, making the larger movements possible.

Both are essential for the movement of the human body.

Vital Nutrients

As a physical trainer, you will be able to help others strengthen their bones through diet and exercise. Essential to the health of bones are nutrients like calcium, vitamin D, and protein.

*   **Calcium** is the mineral responsible for building and maintaining bone density. Without enough calcium, bones can become weak and brittle, increasing the likelihood of breaking bones.

*   **Vitamin D** helps the body absorb calcium. Without enough vitamin D, the bones are not able to use calcium effectively, and the results can be the same as if the body were not getting enough calcium.

*   **Protein** is a nutrient that helps bones build themselves up. When the body is not getting enough protein to fuel vital organs, it will take the protein from the storage in our bones, which can cause fractures.

Strengthening Bones

Bones are strengthened any time a person puts a manageable level of stress on them. The two best kinds of exercise for building bone density are weight-bearing exercises and resistance training. Bone changes to accommodate the force placed on it. These kinds of exercises demonstrate to the body that there are consistent forces placed upon it that demand denser and more capable bones.

The importance of the skeletal system includes movement but also includes support, protection, blood cell production, and fat storage. It is vital to keep a system like this healthy and strong as it continues to grow and strengthen throughout life. There are many aspects of the skeletal system to be aware of, including the axial and appendicular skeletons, the vertebral column, the intervertebral discs, and joints. However, the health of all these aspects can be improved through diet and exercise, ensuring good mobility.

The Muscular System

At the center of all movement lies the muscular system, which is responsible for all the actions we perform. Without the muscular system, no movement would be possible, whether that is breaking a weightlifting record or the involuntary twitch of an eyelid. Muscles are essential to movement, but they also assist the bones in stabilizing joints and maintaining posture. They are also responsible for generating body heat.

The muscular system is made up of muscle fibers, specialized cells that are excellent at contraction. Thousands of these muscle fibers join together to form muscles, which are attached through tendons to bones.

How Muscles Work

Muscles contract when two proteins, myosin and actin, work together to generate force. The myosin filaments pull at the actin filaments, pulling them closer together and shortening the muscle fiber. The shortening of the muscle in this way creates muscle contraction in a process called the sliding filament theory.

To begin this process, the nervous system sends an electrical signal to the muscle, a process called excitation-contraction coupling. First, the brain sends out the nerve impulse, which travels down the motor neuron and communicates the need for movement. When the nerve impulse hits the neuromuscular junction, where the motor neuron meets the muscle, the nerve ending will release a chemical called acetylcholine.

The acetylcholine binds to receptors on the muscle cells, changing their electrical charge. This change releases calcium into the muscle, which binds to the troponin protein allowing actin to be exposed so that myosin will bind to it, and the muscle will contract.

Although the human body may contract a muscle to varying degrees, the muscle fibers themselves operate on an all-or-nothing principle. A fiber either has actin and myosin bind or it does not. It either fully contracts or it does not contract at all. The only thing that determines how much the muscle contracts is how many muscle fibers are contracting at the same time.

Muscle Fibers can be categorized into two types.

1. **Type I fibers** excel at endurance. While they are slower, they can keep up sustained movement for a long time without fatigue.
2. **Type II fibers** excel at quick bursts of activity. They wear out more quickly but can initiate powerful movements.

Gross and Fine Motor Skills

The muscular system has an important role to play in the development of gross and fine motor skills.

*   **Gross motor skills** involve large muscle groups and are some of the first skills for infants and children to develop. This includes skills like walking, crawling, and jumping.
*   **Fine motor skills** involve smaller muscle groups working to create precise movements. These skills are developed after gross motor skills, which is why children can run and jump before they can button a shirt.

The muscular system is the main player in all the movement that takes place in the human body. It is responsible for movement, stability, posture, and body heat. Composed of millions of muscle fibers, this system uses a complex interplay of electrical and chemical reactions that allow for muscle contraction, including the sliding filament theory and excitation-contraction coupling. The muscular system can be strengthened and improved over time, as is demonstrated in the development of gross and fine motor skills.

Cardiorespiratory, Endocrine, and Digestive Systems

The cardiorespiratory, endocrine, and digestive systems work together to keep the human body healthy and energized. An understanding of these systems is vital to a physical trainer. These systems maintain energy levels, regulate metabolism, and supply essential nutrients. Each of these systems impacts the others, and an issue with one can lead to an impact on a person's overall physical abilities.

The Cardiorespiratory System

The cardiorespiratory system refers to the interplay between the cardiovascular system, which is made up of the heart and lungs, and the respiratory system, which is made up of the lungs and airways. This system obtains and circulates essential compounds throughout the body, including things like oxygen, energy, vitamins, and minerals. This is imperative to the human body, as the oxygen and nutrients provide the energy necessary to complete tasks.

The cardiovascular system is made up of two main parts.

1. **The heart**, which pumps blood throughout the body through rhythmic contractions. It is contained in the thoracic cavity, between the lungs. The heart is split up into two atria and two ventricles, one of each on the left and one on the right. On the right side, the heart receives blood that is low on oxygen and sends it through the pulmonary circuit to replace carbon dioxide with oxygen. On the left side, the heart pumps out the oxygenated blood to the rest of the body. The heart has a total of four valves. The mitral and tricuspid valves move blood from the upper chambers of

the heart to the lower chambers of the heart. The aortic and pulmonary valves move blood to the rest of the body.
2. **The blood vessels.** These are hollow tubes that transport the blood to and from the heart. There are three types of blood vessels. Arteries carry blood from the heart, veins carry blood back to the heart, and capillaries are exchange sites for chemicals to go between blood and tissue. The pulmonary artery and vein are especially important, as they carry deoxygenated and oxygenated blood to the heart and lungs respectively.

This entire system is built around blood. Blood supplies the body with the necessary oxygen and nutrients. Red blood cells carry oxygen, white blood cells detect and fight off infections, and platelets stop bleeding.

The body is good at adapting to changing needs, so a person's resting heart rate will change to meet the demands that are placed on it. However, the resting heart rate is usually between 60 and 100 beats per minute. During exercise, the heart rate will increase to meet the elevated oxygen needs. During sleep, the heart rate will decrease. The rhythm of the heart is controlled by the electrical conduction system. The sinus node generates an electrical stimulus at regular intervals, causing the atria to contract.

The Stroke Volume

The stroke volume is the amount of blood pumped by a ventricle in one heartbeat. End-diastolic volume refers to the blood volume in the ventricles before contraction, and end-systolic refers to the amount of blood remaining in the ventricle after the heart has contracted.

A person can calculate the cardiac output, or the amount of blood pumped by the heart in a minute, by multiplying stroke volume and heart rate. Blood pressure measures when the heart contracts (systolic) and when it relaxes (diastolic). Normal blood pressure can fall anywhere from 90/60 mm Hg to 120/80 mm Hg.

The respiratory system

The respiratory system brings in oxygen and expels carbon dioxide. The respiratory system is made up of the airways, lungs, and respiratory muscles.

- **The airways** are made up of the nasal cavity, which is where air enters; the pharynx, which is the passage for both air and food; the larynx, which closes during swallowing to avoid food or liquid from entering the trachea; and the trachea, which carries air from the larynx into the lungs.
- **The lungs** are made up of bronchi, which is where the trachea divides to filter into other lungs; the bronchioles, which are the tiny airways that extend deep into the lungs; and the alveoli, which are the sacs where oxygen and carbon dioxide are exchanged.
- **Respiratory muscles** consist of the diaphragm, which contracts and relaxes to cause inhalation and exhalation; the intercostal muscles, which elevate the rib cage during inhalation and assist in exhalation, and accessory muscles that assist in expanding the chest.

Diffusion of Gasses

Gases move from areas of high concentration to areas of low concentration in a process called diffusion. Gases will try to achieve a state of equilibrium in the respiratory system, as oxygen diffuses from the alveoli into the bloodstream, and carbon dioxide diffuses from the blood into the alveoli, where it is expelled from the body.

When breathing, there are two distinct phases: inhalation and exhalation.

1. **Inhalation**, where the diaphragm contracts, and the intercostal muscles expand the chest cavity, allowing the air to rush in.
2. **Exhalation**, where the diaphragm and intercostal muscles relax, and the air is expelled in the compression. At rest, the respiratory rate can be anywhere from twelve to twenty breaths per minute. However, many factors will influence the breaths per minute.

During heavy breathing, like when a person is exercising, additional muscles will help expand the chest cavity. This assists the body as it attempts to deliver more oxygen. Some breathing patterns are detrimental to oxygen delivery. If a respiratory rate is above or below the normal range of twelve to twenty breaths a minute, there may be health concerns.

Abnormal breathing or respiratory rates will negatively impact exercise performance. A lack of oxygen will lead to fatigue, a lack of endurance, decreased capability, overexertion, and poor recovery. Monitoring signs of abnormal breathing patterns, like shallow or rapid breathing, can allow a physical trainer to help clients avoid these issues.

The cardiorespiratory system, as the system that delivers oxygen and nutrients throughout the body, is vitally important. The heart circulates the oxygen and nutrient-filled blood throughout a network of blood vessels. The lungs and airways oxygenate the blood through an exchange of oxygen and carbon dioxide. When this system functions well, health and physical performance improve, as the body can meet the increased oxygen demands during exercise.

The Endocrine System

The endocrine system has an essential role in the function of the body. This system communicates with the body through hormones that influence growth, development, and metabolism. Unlike the nervous system, which sends messages in microseconds, the endocrine sends generalized chemical messages that are slow-acting but long-lasting. This system regulates a wide variety of functions throughout the body.

The endocrine system is controlled by the hypothalamus and pituitary gland, which coordinate the release of different chemicals through two major categories of glands within the body.

1. **The hypothalamus** directs many automatic functions, like temperature regulation, hunger, thirst, and circadian rhythms. It also controls the actions of the pituitary gland, inhibiting or allowing the release of chemicals, because it monitors the equilibrium of the body to enact the correct responses.
2. **The pituitary gland** releases several hormones of its own but also controls the functions of other glands across the body.

There are two types of glands in the body.

1. **The exocrine glands** have ducts leading to the surface. For instance, sweat glands are exocrine glands.
2. **The endocrine glands** are ductless, meaning that they do not carry anything to the surface. They secrete hormones directly into the blood, which are carried throughout the body.

When the hormones from endocrine glands are secreted into the bloodstream, they regulate physiological functions. They affect only the specific cells and organs that have receptors that can recognize that particular hormone. When the hormone meets a cell with a receptor, it will bind to it, creating cellular responses. The effects of these hormones vary depending on the chemical. When the amount of a certain hormone becomes too high or low, the body will increase or decrease the hormone production.

Here are some important hormones to remember:

1. **Cortisol**, which is released when the body is stressed. To help the body better deal with stressors, cortisol makes more sugar in the body, providing a much-needed energy boost. It reduces inflammation and regulates wakefulness, but can also weaken the immune system and raise blood pressure over time. It helps the body deal with challenges, but when presented with too many stressors, it will become overwhelmed.
2. **Insulin** lowers blood sugar by allowing cells to use the sugar for energy. Every time a person eats, their body releases insulin to keep blood sugar from getting too high.
3. **Glucagon** raises blood sugar when it is too low. When a person has not eaten for a while, glucagon causes the liver to release stored sugar into the blood. Together, insulin and glucagon hormones regulate energy by maintaining a good level of sugar in the blood.
4. **Catecholamines** are a kind of hormone that is also very important. In times of stress, these hormones help a person stay alert, triggering the "fight or flight" response. Some of these chemicals are adrenaline and norepinephrine, which increase heart rate, raise blood pressure, dilate airways, and redirect blood flow. These hormones also activate the lipase enzymes in fat tissue. Lipolysis breaks down fat into fatty acids and glycerol.

The fatty acids can then enter the bloodstream and be used for energy. Like cortisol, these hormones are very beneficial in times of stress, but overexposure to stress can have negative health consequences.

5. **Testosterone**, which promotes muscle growth and repair. Testosterone increases temporarily during exercise to deal with physical stress. When this spike in testosterone levels takes place, the body understands that it needs to be more capable of handling physical stress. Testosterone helps the muscles recover and grow so the body will be better prepared for challenges in the future.

6. **Growth hormones** are also important to the growth and repair of bones and muscles. This hormone is produced in the anterior pituitary gland and can be influenced by a variety of factors. When growth hormones bind to liver receptors, it creates growth factor 1, which grows and repairs body tissues and manages glucose and fat.

7. **Thyroid hormones**, which regulate the body's metabolism, energy production, growth, heart rate, and body temperature. When the hypothalamus decides that thyroid hormones are too low, the thyroid gland will secrete several different hormones into the bloodstream.

During anaerobic resistance training and aerobic activity, these hormones are stimulated. Adrenaline and norepinephrine increase heart rate and energy available in the bloodstream. Insulin helps provide additional energy to the muscles. Cortisol increases the energy production. Growth hormone repairs muscle fibers that were damaged during exercise. Testosterone can also help with muscle growth and repair. Thyroid hormones can also be better regulated through exercise.

Importance of Sleep

One of the most valuable exercises that a person can do to regulate metabolism, hormone function, and muscle recovery is to sleep. When a person is asleep, insulin's effectiveness improves, meaning that without enough sleep, cells do not respond as well to insulin. Over time, a lack of sleep will negatively impact the body's ability to maintain blood sugar levels. The production of many hormones relies on sleep, but two hormones are particularly affected by inadequate sleep.

Growth hormone is almost exclusively released during sleep, meaning that without sufficient sleep, one of the key components to muscle growth is missing. Cortisol is also affected by sleep, as it follows the body's circadian rhythms, and will be disrupted if a person does not follow this rhythm. Sleep is also the time in which the body does the majority of its repair work.

If the body does not get this time to repair itself, it will cause muscle fatigue and delayed recovery.

As a physical trainer, it is essential to be aware of the functions of the endocrine system. The release of hormones has a slow but profound impact on the body and its ability to perform in exercise. The production of these hormones, controlled by the hypothalamus and pituitary gland, maintains equilibrium in the body. Although the endocrine system largely monitors itself, a person can help its efficacy by not overstressing the body and getting enough sleep.

The Digestive System

The digestive system also has an important role to play in the overall health of the body. Exercise can help improve digestive function. The digestive system includes the digestive tract and the accessory organs:

1. Mouth
2. Pharynx,
3. Esophagus
4. Stomach,
5. Small intestine, which digests and absorbs nutrients, water, and electrolytes
6. Large intestine, which continues to absorb water and electrolytes, ferments carbohydrates and fiber, and forms feces.

Other organs, like the salivary glands, liver, gallbladder, and pancreas are responsible for secreting necessary fluids into the digestive tract, working to break down and absorb food. The liver also aids in the metabolic process and detoxifies the blood. The tongue and teeth also aid in digestion.

The Digestive Process

The digestive process goes through these steps:

1. **Ingestion,** which means taking in food.
2. **Digestion,** which has two stages.

   a. **Mechanical digestion,** which includes chewing in the mouth and mixing in the stomach.
   b. **Chemical digestion,** where complex molecules are turned into smaller molecules. This process uses water and digestive enzymes to break down these molecules.

3. **Absorption and elimination**, where molecules that can be absorbed are, and molecules that cannot are eliminated.

The main role of exercise in the digestive process is that it maintains equilibrium. Exercise helps maintain a healthy weight, which reduces digestive issues like acid reflux and takes pressure off the stomach. It also reduces stress, which can exacerbate digestive issues.

Human Movement Science

Three anatomical body planes describe how the human body moves.

1. **The coronal (frontal) plane** separates the front and back of the body, with all movements running along this plane, never crossing it. The movements described along this plane are abduction, adduction, elevation, depression, and inversion and eversion of the ankle.
2. **The sagittal (longitudinal) plane** separates the left and right sides of the body, with all movement running parallel to this line. The movements described along this plane are flexion, extension, dorsiflexion, and plantar flexion.
3. **The transverse (axial) plane** separates the upper and lower halves of the body, with all movements rotating around this axis. The movements described along this plane are rotation and horizontal abduction and adduction.

Movement is described using anatomical position, where the body is standing with arms down and palms facing forward. From that position, trainers can describe movements concerning this base position. They can describe a location as:

- **Medial:** situated in the middle
- **Lateral:** from the side
- **Contralateral:** pertaining to the other side
- **Ipsilateral:** affecting the same side of the body
- **Anterior:** in the front of the body
- **Posterior:** in the back of the body
- **Proximal:** nearer to the center
- **Distal:** further from the center
- **Inferior:** towards the bottom
- **Superior:** towards the top

Another concept that is important when describing movement is the difference between osteokinematics and arthrokinematics:

- **Osteokinematics** describes the visible movements of the bones at the joints. These movements are easy to see and identify.
- **Arthrokinematics** describes the movements that take place inside the joint, making the larger movements possible.

Movement

There is a wide variety of movements that are vital to understand, including:

- **Retraction:** movement inward
- **Protraction:** movement outward
- **Depression:** movement downwards
- **Elevation:** movement upwards

Muscle actions are broken into three main divisions.

1. **Isotonic action,** where there is a contraction of a muscle resulting in joint movement. These actions can be either concentric or eccentric.

    a. **Concentric** means the muscle shortens when producing force, like the upward motion of a bicep curl.
    b. **Eccentric** means the muscle lengthens when producing force, like the lowering motion in a bicep curl.

2. **Isometric action,** which create muscle tension without a change in muscle length or visible joint movement, like pushing against a brick wall.
3. **Isokinetic action** has a fixed speed of movement as resistance varies with the force exerted, which only occurs under controlled conditions.

In concentric and eccentric actions, there is the possibility of placing a muscle in an overly shortened or lengthened position, which means that the muscle has a limited ability to produce force and could cause muscle strain. Exercises should be done within the normal range of movement. Stretching before exercise can also mitigate the risk of injury due to these issues.

When a muscle abruptly changes from an eccentric to a concentric contraction, it is called a stretch-shortening cycle. This cycle consists of three phases:

1. **Eccentric,** where the muscle stretches and prepares to generate force
2. **Amortization,** which is the split-second transition point where the stored energy is released
3. **Concentric,** where the muscle shortens while generating force.

During movement, a muscle can fulfill four different roles, comprising the global muscular system.

1. **Agonist,** which is the muscle directly responsible for the movement.
2. **Antagonist,** which is the muscle that opposes the agonist, relaxing or slowing a movement while the agonist contracts.
3. **Synergist,** which is the muscles that assist the agonist.
4. **Fixator,** which keeps the origin of the muscle steady.

When multiple forces act in different directions to cause a rotational motion, this is called a **force couple**. The local muscular system is responsible for stabilizing joints during movement. They also maintain good posture, assist in balance and coordination, and minimize stress on the joints.

There are also two different ways in which the end of a limb interacts with the ground during movement.

1. **Closed-chain movements** mean that the end of the limb is making contact with the ground, meaning that the limb is pushing against the ground.
2. **Open-chain movements** mean that the distal end is not fixed. It does not bear the body's weight and can move freely. This is often used to isolate the movement of a particular joint.

If a person were to describe the movements of leg exercises, squats are closed-chain, and leg extensions are open-chain.

The muscles depend on many factors to produce force, including tension. Tension refers to the amount of force that is built up when the muscle contracts. This contraction depends on the amount of overlap between the filaments of a muscle.

The body's muscles can be divided into three different groups of levers.

1. **A first-class lever** has a fulcrum in the middle.
2. **A second-class lever** has resistance in the middle and effort on one side.
3. **A third-class lever** has effort between the resistance and the fulcrum.

Proprioception

Proprioception is the body's ability to sense its position and movement. Despite not looking at your limbs, you know where they are. This sense helps you maintain balance and coordination.

Motor skills

Motor neurons provide both the signals from the brain to the muscles and feedback from the muscles to the brain. The feedback that is gained from the motor neurons can help a person learn motor skills and physical movements. Motor learning explains the process of acquiring skills, retaining, transferring, adapting, and correcting motor skills. By learning and improving motor skills, a person can enhance their exercise performance.

Understanding the movement of the human body is essential as we strive to help others improve their movement ability. Understanding the anatomical planes and terminology allows personal trainers to describe movements accurately and clearly. Many concepts behind movement are essential to understand, such as the difference between osteokinematics and arthrokinematics, the roles of muscles, force couples, closed and open-chain movement, levers, and proprioception. However, understanding these concepts helps individuals learn and improve their motor skills.

Exercise Metabolism and Bioenergetics

The need for the body to have energy is a recurring theme in the study of human movement. For the body to function properly, the body requires a steady supply of energy. The main form of energy used in the body is **adenosine triphosphate (ATP)**, which comes from the energy provided by food sources. The first law of thermodynamics explains that energy cannot be created or destroyed, just converted from one form to another. The energy gained from food must be converted into substrates before it is usable. For instance, ATP is converted from carbohydrates, fats, and proteins.

When carbohydrates are broken down, they become glucose and are absorbed into the blood. Glucose is the simple sugar that serves as the primary source of energy for the body. When there is too much glucose in the blood, the body will store it as glycogen, the complex sugar that is used when there is no glucose available.

Glycogen is stored in the liver and muscles. About 100 grams can be stored in the liver, and about 500 can be stored in the muscles. Fat, however, can be stored throughout the body, with a wide range of body fat percentages.

There are three pathways for metabolism.

1. **The ATP pathway**, which supplies the energy needed in the first ten to fifteen seconds of an activity. It provides short bursts of quick energy, relying on the creatine in the muscles.
2. **Glycolysis**, used for the next thirty to sixty seconds after the ATP pathway. It converts energy from glucose.
3. **Oxidative phosphorylation**, which uses mainly oxygen for energy, though it also pulls from fats. This pathway is used for endurance activities and creates carbon dioxide and water as byproducts. Because carbon dioxide is one of the byproducts, respiration rates increase during exercise. However, if respiration rates become too high, a person can hyperventilate, become dizzy or lightheaded, and decrease the amount of oxygen that is delivered.

The two factors that determine the type of energy used are duration and intensity. These two factors are inversely related. The higher the intensity, the shorter the activity, and vice versa. An exercise can also be performed as a steady-state activity (continuing the same steady level of exertion) or as an intermittent activity (switching between high and low intensity).

During high-intensity workouts, most ATP will come from carbohydrates. During low-intensity workouts, most ATP will come from fats. However, if a low-intensity activity goes on for long enough, it will begin to pull more ATP from carbohydrates.

When a person's energy requirements match the amount of energy they take in through food, they are in an **energy balance**, where their weight will remain constant. Calories are burned through a combination of these factors:

- **Resting metabolic rate**, which refers to the number of calories needed to function at rest (60-75% of the total).
- **Thermic effect** of food refers to the calories needed to digest food (10% of the total).
- **Exercise and non-exercise activity** burn about 15-30% of the total.

The combination of these factors creates a person's total daily expenditure, or how many calories are required to meet their daily needs.

Free fatty acids

Free fatty acids are an important part of fats, created when triglycerides are broken down. They are used by the body for energy. Through a process called beta-oxidation, free fatty acids can be oxidized, meaning that they can be used for energy. This process begins when stored fat is broken down. The free fatty acids are then moved to cells and bind with coenzyme A. This bond then moves to the mitochondria of the cell and is broken down until it releases acetyl-CoA. It then goes through the Krebs cycle to create ATP.

Amino acids

Amino acids are the molecules that combine to form protein. They can be metabolized through transamination, deamination, and catabolism. Transamination means changing one amino acid into another by transferring an amino group. Deamination removes the amino group, creating ammonia, which can then be changed into urea. Catabolism breaks down the amino acids, converting them into energy. In healthy bodies, amino acids can be used to repair tissue, produce enzymes, create energy, regulate hormones, improve the immune system, and produce neurotransmitters.

Ketone bodies

Ketone bodies are produced from the fatty acids in the liver. They include acetone, acetoacetic acid, and beta-hydroxybutyric acid. When there are not enough carbohydrates in the body, they can be oxidized to create energy. To be oxidized, ketone bodies are converted into acetyl-CoA. It then goes through the Krebs cycle to produce ATP.

Nutrition

Personal trainers are not authorized to provide nutrition counseling, medical nutrition therapy, and meal plans. This is the responsibility of registered dietitians, certified nutritionists, CISSNs, CNSs, and CDNs or LDNs. However, personal trainers should have a good base understanding of nutrition, as clients may ask for general advice. Any advice should be credible, meaning that the source is reputable, the person giving the information is qualified, the information is supported by other research, and it has been reviewed by professionals.

Protein

Protein is made of amino acids, with nine amino acids being essential to get through diet and eleven that can be gained through diet or manufactured in the body. Protein is essential to the body because it repairs cells and tissues. It also synthesizes hormones, enzymes, antibodies, and peptides, and transports compounds throughout the body.

Proteins are complete when they have, at the least, all essential amino acids. When they lack one or more amino acids, they are incomplete. Animal-based proteins, like meat, eggs, and milk, are complete protein sources, although there are some plant-based complete proteins, like quinoa and soy. Many other plant sources are incomplete, like vegetables, rice, and beans. However, by combining different incomplete proteins, a person can still get all the necessary amino acids. There are four calories in every gram of protein.

For protein, the recommended daily allowance (RDA) is 0.8 grams per kilogram of body weight. This amount will meet the nutritional needs of most people. The range that is associated with a reduced risk of chronic disease, or the acceptable macronutrient distribution range (AMDR), is anywhere from 10% to 35% of daily caloric intake. However, these amounts may be adjusted due to individual circumstances. For instance, most athletes will need more protein than the recommended allowance.

Carbohydrates

Carbohydrates are the main source of energy for the body during activity. They are compounds that include carbon, hydrogen, and oxygen atoms. They can be:

- **Simple sugars** like glucose, fructose, and galactose, which come from foods that contain quickly digestible sugars, like honey, sugar, and candy.
- **Disaccharides** like sucrose, maltose, and lactose
- **Polysaccharides** like starch, glycogen, and fiber
- **Complex carbohydrates** come from foods that take longer to break down, meaning they are a more sustained source of energy. These carbohydrates can be found in whole grains, starchy vegetables, beans, and fiber.
- **Fiber,** which is an important carbohydrate because the body does not absorb it. Instead, it continues through the digestive system largely intact and plays a role in digestive and heart health. It can also help maintain more stable blood sugar levels.

Depending on the amount of exercise, a person can require anywhere from three to twelve grams of carbohydrates per kilogram of body weight. For fiber, the recommended amount is more straightforward. Between the ages of nineteen and fifty, men should get 38 grams, and women should get 25 grams.

The Glycemic Index and Glycemic Load

The **glycemic index** is a rating system for how quickly a carbohydrate will raise the amount of sugar in the blood. The more complex a carbohydrate is, the slower blood sugar levels will rise, and the lower the rating on the glycemic index.

However, the **glycemic load** is frequently considered a better system for indicating a carbohydrate's impact on blood sugar levels. It takes into account the portion sizes, which will impact how quickly the carbohydrates are absorbed. It also considers the combination of all the foods included in the meal, rather than isolating one ingredient.

When there is too much glucose in the bloodstream, the body will convert some of this to glycogen. This glycogen can be stored in the liver and muscles, but the amount of storage space is limited. The glycogen can be released from the liver if blood sugar is too low.

Lipids

There are three different kinds of lipids.

1. **Triglycerides,** which have a glycerol backbone and three fatty acid chains. These include three kinds of fats:

   a. **Saturated fats,** which can be found in many places, including fatty cuts of meat, baked goods, and coconut oil.
   b. **Polyunsaturated fats,** which can be found in fatty fish, walnuts, and sunflower seed oil.
   c. **Monounsaturated fats,** which can be found in olive oil, peanuts, and avocados

2. **Phospholipids,** which have a glycerol backbone, two fatty acid chains, and a phosphate molecule. Phospholipids can be found in eggs, soy, or liver.
3. **Sterols,** which have a ring of carbon and hydrogen atoms. They are also known as fats, and are a great concentrated energy source. Sterols can be found in eggs, fish, and nuts.

Whatever the source, lipids contain nine calories per gram. The AMDR for lipids is around 20-35% of the total daily calories.

Micronutrients and Hydration

Micronutrients include vitamins, minerals, and phytonutrients.

1. **Vitamins:** Different vitamins provide different benefits to the body, but all vitamins are essential. The two different groups of vitamins are water-soluble and fat-soluble. Water-soluble vitamins dissolve in water and include vitamin C and all B vitamins. Fat-soluble vitamins dissolve in fat and include A, D, and K. Eating from a wide variety of food groups is the best way to ensure that a person gets an adequate amount of vitamins.
2. **Minerals:** These are compounds that perform a variety of tasks throughout

the body. There are macrominerals, which include calcium, magnesium, potassium, and sodium, and there are microminerals, which include chromium, cobalt, copper, fluoride, iodine, iron, manganese, molybdenum, selenium, and zinc.

3. **Phytonutrients:** these chemicals are found in plants and are beneficial for general health and in the prevention of diseases. There are thousands of phytonutrients that are found in plant foods.

Hydration

For proper hydration, men should get 15.5 cups of fluid a day, and women should get 11.5. During a workout that lasts longer than 60 minutes, it may be helpful to add carbohydrates to fluid intake, and drink 4-8 ounces every twenty minutes. Athletes should aim to replace the fluid lost during an event. The amount of fluid lost will vary depending on intensity and duration of the exercise.

Sports drinks are specifically made to replace electrolytes and help the body rehydrate. Isotonic drinks contain sugars and electrolytes in an amount designed to mimic the body's fluids, directly replacing them.

1. **Hypotonic drinks** contain less sugars and electrolytes than body fluids do, designed with the purpose of rehydration without the calories.
2. **Hypertonic drinks** contain more sugars and electrolytes than body fluids do, with the purpose of replenishing glycogen stores. Because they do not hydrate well, they are typically consumed after a workout, rather than during.
3. **Protein drinks** provide carbohydrates, electrolytes, and protein, used for recovery after a workout in order to support muscle repair. During short, low-intensity activity, sports drinks are likely not necessary. They are also not necessary during day to day activities.

Nutrition Strategies

Nutrition strategies are determined by many factors, including the person's body composition, BMR, height, weight, and ability to gain and lose weight. These strategies serve to improve something about a person's health, including things like energy, performance, body composition, disease, cognitive capacity, recovery, and weight management.

As you approach nutrition strategies, it's important to remember the first law of thermodynamics, which is that energy is not created or destroyed, it only changes forms. Weight can be influenced by this law of thermodynamics, sleep, endocrine disorders, medications, metabolism, and adaptive thermogenesis.

Weight gain is typically caused by consuming more calories than are used, whether by eating more or by burning less. However, genetics, medication, and hormones have the potential to cause weight gain. Weight loss is typically caused by consuming fewer calories than are used, whether by eating less or burning more.

No matter what the nutrition strategy, all have a similar focus. They all promote balanced diets with a large amount of variety, in order to ensure a variety of nutrients.

Food Labels

Food labels give consumers vital information about the foods they are eating. They can be used to make decisions based on the information provided. Most food labels will include serving sizes, how many servings are in the container and the amounts of sugar, sodium, and cholesterol, and various vitamins and minerals.

When attempting to lose weight, some of the important factors to consider are the amount of calories (both per unit and per serving), the amount of fat, the amount of sugars, and the recommended amounts.

To increase muscle mass, the essential element is the amount of protein, as that is the nutrient that will build and strengthen muscles.

When reading food labels, it is important to keep in mind the energy needed. Even if a person is trying to lose weight, their body still needs the calories and nutrients supplied by foods.

It can be helpful to eat at regular intervals throughout the day. Doing so will provide consistency for the body, leading to a steady supply of energy and a stable blood sugar level. It will also help regulate appetite, as skipping meals will cause the need to make up for them later.

Maintaining a good level of hydration is also important. Water is essential for nearly everything the body does. It helps with endurance, cognitive ability, temperature regulation, and weight management. By eating and drinking consistently, a person will have a consistent level of performance.

Supplements

Diet supplements are meant to add—or supplement—some key nutrients that may be lacking in a diet. As such, they are not meant to replace a diet. However, they can be a valuable tool to help provide nutrients. They contain a variety of ingredients, including vitamins, minerals, and amino acids.

In the United States, dietary supplements are regulated by the FDA. Labels on supplements are similar to food, but if they have a small enough amount of an ingredient, they do not have to list it.

When used to enhance performance, supplements are called ergogenic. However, supplements can also help people improve general health through gaining enough vitamins, minerals, omega-3, or protein.

Many athletes take supplements that contain protein, creatine, and caffeine. When struggling to get enough protein through diet, protein supplements can help a person with muscle repair and growth. Depending on activity level, an effective dose of protein is around 0.5 grams per pound. An effective dose of creatine is from 3-5 grams, and caffeine is effective at around 3 kilograms per pound.

Despite the benefits of supplements, it is important to never go above the tolerable upper intake level (UL). Exceeding this limit can lead to toxicity. It is also important to note that some ergogenic supplements are banned or illegal to use.

Personal trainers can give clients general advice on nutrition and supplements, but it is best to refer them to professionals in these areas. A personal trainer can never give a client a prescription.

Although this may seem like a lot of information to cover, it is imperative for a personal trainer to understand the functions of the human body. A physical trainer focuses on movement, which is not possible without the nervous, skeletal, and muscular systems. They also understand the impact of the cardiorespiratory, endocrine, and digestive systems on physical well-being. At the center of this knowledge is the application through human movement. And although a personal trainer may not give specific directions on nutrition, they should have a basic understanding in order to give general advice to their client. That is why all this information will be covered on the exam.

Chapter Summary

- In order to design an effective training plan, a physical trainer must have an understanding of the body's eleven organ systems, particularly the nervous, muscular, skeletal, cardiorespiratory, endocrine, and digestive systems.
- The nervous system is essential for movement, sensation and cognitive processes.
- Calcium, vitamin d, and weight-bearing exercises can help strengthen bone support, protection, and movement.
- The muscular system, essential for all movement, is built from muscle fibers and can be strengthened through motor skill development and exercise.
- The cardiorespiratory system, based around the heart and lungs, is essential for delivering oxygen and nutrients.
- The endocrine system uses hormones to regulate bodily functions, including cortisol, insulin, and growth hormones.
- Understanding human movement is essential for personal trainers, including anatomical planes, muscle actions, osteokinematics, arthrokinematics, and the roles of muscles in movement.
- Carbohydrates, fats, and proteins are converted into ATP for energy.

In the next chapter, you will learn more about how to go beyond practical knowledge and into relationships with your clients.

Chapter Three: Client Relations and Behavioral Coaching

People view exercise differently because people have different body ideals. Perception of the correct way to exercise is informed by a variety of factors, including images from the media. Unfortunately, many of these media images do not create a healthy perception of what a human body should look like, or what outcomes can be expected from exercise. It is important to help clients understand that physical appearance is not always the best indicator of health. While a personal trainer can help an individual achieve a certain look through training, the individual's health and safety should inform the decisions.

Exercise can be performed for physical appearance, health, or improved performance, depending on the individual's values. However, it is rare to obtain all three at the same time. A person frequently has to choose which one will receive top priority. For instance, a powerlifter may need to keep a higher body fat percentage to fuel his performance, while a bodybuilder may weaken their performance to have the desired physical appearance. A person's combination of experiences and feelings changes how they view exercise, and which goals they approach it with.

A personal trainer needs to be prepared to explain the trade-offs between pursuing different goals. Communicating clearly with the client about expectations will allow them to share what aspects of exercise are most important to them, and to gain a better understanding of their experiences and feelings regarding exercise.

The Psychology of Exercise

Psychology explains how the mind influences behaviors. To create a behavior change, like exercising when they haven't before, a person needs to understand the role their mind plays in the development of a new habit. While psychologists and psychiatrists are both experts in mental health, understanding the creation of a habit is an important aspect of psychology for physical trainers. Understanding the factors that influence motivation and habit creation assists them in creating more effective program designs and in better supporting their clients along the way. Exercise and sports psychology is the specific study of the psychological factors in the performance of a physical activity.

Motivation

Motivation is the reason why a person does what they do. It describes both the intensity and direction of their behaviors. The greater the motivation, the greater the enthusiasm for the behavior. More enthusiasm means that the person will be more willing to invest time, effort, and energy into making a change. Reasons for a behavior may change over time, so it is important to reevaluate as circumstances change. Reevaluating motivations helps keep goals relevant and helps the client feel the impact of their progression. For instance, a weight loss goal may become a weight maintenance goal as the client reaches their desired weight.

There are two types of motivation:

1. External motivation focuses on doing something for a reward.
2. Internal motivation focuses on the enjoyment of doing something as its own reward.

To follow through with a behavior, both these types of motivation are important. Often, individuals begin with the external motivator as the primary reason for exercise. As they continue to exercise, they will begin to find aspects of exercise that they enjoy. Then, even when the external rewards are lacking, they will find a reason to keep going.

Motivation helps people overcome barriers that keep them from exercising. Some common barriers include time, unrealistic goals, lack of social support, inconvenience, social physique anxiety, and ambivalence. While these barriers are generalized, a physical trainer should explore with their client to understand what obstacles are in their way. However, many clients will experience one of these reasons as a barrier to achieving their goals.

Time Management

The lack of time can be solved by helping a client address their approach to time management. By identifying the motivators for the client, the personal trainer can help them realize that they would like to find time to exercise. For some, creating a way to schedule and be accountable for their time will be the most beneficial. This way, they have pre-determined times that they will exercise, with time-efficient workouts. For others, the best course of action is to allow them flexibility while still having some consistency. Allowing them to adjust their schedules and be okay with mistakes will take away some of the stress that comes from an overly precise schedule.

Unrealistic Goals

Unrealistic goals can be solved by helping the client set realistic goals. Listen to the client's goals to determine whether the goal is truly unrealistic, or if it is just not within their capabilities at the time frame they have in mind. Help the client understand the difference between a focus on an outcome (like placing in a race) and on progress (like increasing the intensity of an exercise). This will help them evaluate what kind of goals they need to be setting.

Social Physique Anxiety

When someone has significant anxiety and insecurity about how others view their appearance they are suffering from social physique anxiety. As the reasons for this anxiety vary, approaches to addressing it will vary based on the client. Some common techniques include empathizing with the client's fears, promoting positive body image, and replacing negative thoughts with positive ones.

Inconvenience

When exercise seems inconvenient, it is helpful to meet the client where they're at. Exercise doesn't have to be done at the gym at a specific time, it can also be done from home at the time most convenient to them. The more consistent they are with their habits, the less it will seem like an inconvenience.

Ambivalence

Ambivalence to exercise comes about when someone has mixed feelings about exercise, like knowing that it is good for them, but disliking the time it takes away from other things. To address ambivalence, a person needs to create further motivation for exercise.

Social Support

Social support and influence are also key to the motivation to exercise. Social influences that are meaningful to a person can be used to motivate them to exercise. A personal trainer can help a client identify the people they can use to help them stay motivated. They can also recommend classes, groups, or workout buddies to help them find new groups. These people can also be used to lend support.

- Instrumental support is the direct action that allows a person to engage in a behavior, like giving them a ride to the gym.
- Emotional support is the encouragement and empathy that can help motivate a person to engage in a behavior. Empathy is particularly important because it allows the person to feel as though someone else truly understands their difficulties.
- Informational support is giving accurate information that enables a person to change behavior.
- Companionship support is when a person engages in a behavior with another person.

This support can be obtained through many groups in a person's life, including family and exercise groups. Parents have a particularly strong influence on a person's approach to exercise. If the parent has a good relationship with exercise, the child is more likely to view it positively. In exercise groups, the exercise leader has a strong influence, as they will set the level of consistency and intensity. Forming an exercise group has many benefits, including accountability and comradery.

Impact on Mental Health

Not only does mental health impact exercise, but exercise can also positively impact mental health. It improves self-esteem and body image, helping a person feel as though they have control over their bodies. Exercise also improves sleep, which is the time that the brain resets and creates new pathways. Regular exercise also reduces the symptoms of anxiety and depression.

Behavioral Coaching

Three things are key to coming across as an effective personal trainer: professionalism, relationship-building, and competency. The client will be more willing to listen to someone who seems like a professional, which includes looking clean, neat, and dressing appropriately. By maintaining the role of a professional, you demonstrate to a client that you are not just a friend offering advice, but someone who is paid for their knowledge and expertise.

Building a relationship with the client will take time, but will also help the client feel as though you know and understand them. This stems from listening to what they want to achieve out of an exercise program and then empathizing with them.

Your competency as a personal trainer will come through as you help your client design an effective training program. Being willing to change the program as the client's goals and needs change demonstrates that you are effective in both the short term and the long term.

Designing a Program

Program designs must be based on the client's abilities and should address their health concerns and goals. A program should also be designed to help them build self-efficacy, i.e., confidence in their abilities to control their behavior, motivation, and performance. Planning and self-monitoring improve self-efficacy, as they demonstrate to the client that they are in charge and are capable of making positive changes.

Positive affective judgments, like when the client views exercise as enjoyable, will improve the likelihood that they will continue to exercise because they have a positive association. The reverse is true when the client views exercise as painful or uncomfortable. Subjective norms, or a person's perception of the expectations of others, will also impact the likelihood that they continue to exercise. If the client believes that others expect them to exercise, they are more likely to do so. However, if they feel as though others doubt them or do not place a priority on health, they are less likely to go against what they feel to be the norm.

Therefore, one of the best ways to assess a client is to understand their readiness to change. Depending on their past experiences, views on exercise, and new goals, they may be more or less prepared to begin the journey. The Transtheoretical Model of Behavior Change explains that people will progress to the point of readiness. In the precontemplation stage, a person does not exercise and will not begin within the next six months. In the contemplation stage, a person does not exercise but is planning to begin within the next six months. In the preparation stage, a person is taking the steps towards exercise, and may even be exercising sporadically. In the action stage, a person has been exercising for less than six months. In the maintenance stage, a person has been exercising consistently for six months or more. Understanding where the client is at will help you best be able to meet their needs.

Communication With the Client

To meet their needs, it is important to pay attention to how you communicate verbally and non-verbally. One of the most important needs of every client is the knowledge that their trainer listens to and respects their opinion. As the expert in movement and exercise, a trainer has more authority than the client. To help them feel valued, good communication and active listening is key.

In verbal communication, pay attention to the words used and how they are said. In non-verbal communication, pay attention to facial expression, posture, and eye contact. Active listening, or asking questions, reflecting, summarizing, affirming, and asking permission, will help your clients feel as though you are listening to them.

A personal trainer can also use motivational interviewing, which is used to enhance internal motivation. This includes observing the discrepancy between the client's current and ideal state, promoting change talk, and assessing readiness, willingness, and perceived ability to change.

Developing a Behavioral Change Technique (BCT)

A BCT is a strategy that will help a client make a change, such as setting goals. Cognitive strategies will help clients by helping them engage in positive self-talk, creating imagery, and psyching them up.

When helping clients set goals, ensure that these goals are specific, measurable, achievable, relevant, and time-bound (SMART).

- **Specific:** it leaves no room for ambiguity, answering the questions of who, what, when, where, and why clearly.
- **Measurable:** it can be monitored, with a clear goal.
- **Achievable:** setting the client up for success by helping them create goals that consider the ability and time that they can invest.
- **Relevant:** it should be in alignment with long-term goals.
- **Time-bound:** it has a deadline, which will help clients avoid procrastination.

Therefore, a goal like, "I want to lose weight" becomes "I want to lose ten pounds in two months." For the best outcome, clients should determine long-term goals and then set smaller goals to help them progress along the way.

Perceptions and motivations will help a client begin to exercise and follow through with goals. They can be aided by social groups and an effective personal trainer. A good personal trainer will help ensure that their goals are realistic, that they stay motivated, and help them feel ready to change. As you help your client set goals and stay motivated, they will improve in their ability to do so.

Chapter Summary

- People exercise for various reasons that include a mixture of appearance, health, and performance.
- Support from family and exercise groups is pivotal to client success.
- Exercise benefits mental health and self-esteem.

In the next chapter, you will learn the importance of assessments and NASM's standard of assessing a client. This will help you better apply the psychology learned here.

Chapter Four: Assessment

Fitness assessment helps a personal trainer be equipped to develop an effective program that is tailored to the client. Reassessment also demonstrates progress to the client as they see improvement in results.

To ensure that the client has no medical conditions that prohibit them from exercising, physical trainers can use the PAR-Q+, which asks seven basic questions about health. If the client answers yes to any of those questions, the physical trainer should advise them to consult a medical professional before beginning a training program.

When there is a need for additional information beyond the PAR-Q+, the physical trainer can collect this information through a health history questionnaire (HHQ). Knowing lifestyle habits, physical limitations, and past injuries helps the physical trainer make more informed decisions.

Assessing Physical Fitness

Once the trainer knows the client will not be at risk if they begin an exercise program, they can assess physical fitness, moving from the least to the most vigorous test.

The Heart

Heart rate is one of the first assessments. NASM recommends measuring the resting heart rate at the radial pulse to prevent putting pressure on the vagus nerve, which can slow the heart response. The heart rate at rest will help determine progress over time as the heart and lungs grow more conditioned. The heart rate during exercise is a good indicator of how much exertion is necessary for the individual to perform an exercise.

Blood Pressure

Blood pressure beyond the normal range of 120/80 can be a cause for concern and should be carefully assessed before beginning any strenuous exercise.

Anthropometry

Anthropometry is the study of the measurement of human beings. There are many different ways to assess the variations in weight, size, and proportion. These measurements are useful as a way to compare health by noninvasively measuring nutritional status and amounts of body fat.

One method for this is the body mass index (BMI). Though very inaccurate, this can be a good starting point for assessing the client. It uses height and weight measurements to assign a number. Below 18.5 is underweight, 18.5-24.9 is healthy, 25-29.9 is overweight, and 30 and above is obese.

However, this does not take into account other variances in weight, such as the lean muscle of an athlete, which leads many muscular people to have a BMI reading of overweight or obese.

Circumference measurement is another method. Measurements at the waist, neck, chest, hips, thighs, calves, and arms can help measure progression as the body changes over time. However, it does not provide much baseline health information, as there is significant variance between body proportions in different people.

Skinfold measures take measurements of areas of the body with a significant amount of fat, such as the biceps, chest, or thigh. This method helps understand the fat percentage, but it takes time to learn this skill.

Bioelectrical Impedance Analysis

A machine passes electricity through the body and analyzes how much muscle and fat is present. Electricity moves differently as it passes through fat and muscle but this can be affected by hydration levels so it is important to test at different times.

Hydrostatic Underwater Weighing

Because bone, muscle, and connective tissue are denser than fat, people will displace the water differently as their fat levels vary. Though fairly accurate, it is an expensive process, involving many calculations based on a variety of factors.

Cardiorespiratory Assessments

Cardiorespiratory assessments measure how able a client is to do work. This allows a personal trainer to plan exercises that do not overexert the client.

The VO2 Max Test

This looks at oxygen consumption and usage based on the difference between inhaled and exhaled oxygen. The higher the VO2 max, the greater the oxygen utilization and ability to do work.

The Talk Test

This is a very informal way of measuring, but it allows the trainer to see how much exercise impacts a person's exertion. While the client is exercising, the trainer will carry on a conversation with them. The trainer then assesses how much difficulty the client has while speaking to determine how much the person is exerting themselves.

The Ventilatory Threshold (VT) Test

VT1 and VT2 tests increase intensity when using the talk test. While doing a cardio activity, the trainer will assess the client's breathing and exertion. In the VT1 stage, breathing is audible and the client is having difficulty catching their breath. This means that they are using both carbohydrates and fat as fuel while exerting themselves. In the VT2 stage, used for clients with performance goals, the client increases intensity until they cannot speak. They are now burning primarily glucose.

Posture, Movement, and Performance Assessments

Assessing posture, movement, and performance can also help inform a physical trainer's decisions as they make an exercise plan. Posture helps decrease stress on the joints, both while static and while in motion.

Static Posture

Static posture is assessed when the body is simply standing. Deviations from the optimal position will cause stress to the joints. Trainers keep an eye out for three main deviations.

1. **Pes planus distortion syndrome**, which involves flat feet, knee valgus, and adducted and internally rotated hips.
2. **Lower crossed syndrome** includes an anterior pelvic tilt and extension of the lumbar spine.
3. **Upper crossed syndrome** involves a forward head and rounded shoulders.

Assessments are made using the kinetic chain checkpoints at feet, ankles, knees, lumbo-pelvic-hip complex, shoulders, head, and neck.

Dynamic Posture

Dynamic posture is assessed when the body is in movement. One of the first and best exercises to assess posture is the overhead squat assessment. It assesses dynamic posture, core stability, and neuromuscular control. It uses all kinetic chain checkpoints, so deviations can be seen throughout, making it the basis for all other movement assessments.

Keep an eye out for feet or knees changing position, back arching, arms falling forward, or difficulty keeping balance.

When clients do very well in an overhead squat, they can be further assessed for strength, balance, and coordination through a single-leg squat assessment. Pushing and pulling assessments can be done to challenge the upper body before or during a workout.

Push-up and Jump Tests

Push-up tests measure muscular endurance in the upper body. For clients with strength goals, a bench press weight assessment that finds a one-rep max will allow the trainer to monitor progress.

A squat strength assessment finds a one-rep max that allows the trainer to monitor progress for clients with strength goals in the lower body.

Vertical and long jump assessments measure max jump and lower body power and are suitable for some clients.

The Lower Extremity Functional Test

This test is an advanced assessment to be used for clients with speed and performance goals. It involves a series of complicated maneuvers in a diamond shape, including running backward, forward, shuffling, crossovers, and figure eights.

The 40-yard dash allows a trainer to monitor the client's ability to react, accelerate, and sprint. The pro shuttle assessment, or 5-10-5, is used only for clients who want to improve speed and control and is used for assessing their ability to accelerate, decelerate, and have control.

Performance Assessments

Using performance assessments regularly will allow a trainer to be aware of the client's progress and baseline. The assessments work best when following this order: health screening, physiological and body composition assessments, postural and movement assessments, cardio assessments, and then performance assessments. The non-fatiguing assessments, which include health screening, physiological assessments, and body composition assessments, should always be done first. Exercise caution when implementing movement and performance assessments. Keep in mind any health concerns and the client's goals.

When used properly, physical assessments can help a trainer tailor an exercise program to a client and track the client's progress. As they use the many tools at their disposal to monitor a client's progress, an effective personal trainer keeps the client's health and personal goals at the forefront.

Chapter Summary

- Physical assessment allows a physical trainer to personalize plans and monitor progress.
- Always use a health history questionnaire to ensure the client is fit for exercise.
- Assessments can look into heart rate, body composition, cardiorespiratory, posture, movement, and performance.

In the next chapter, you will learn how to move beyond assessment and into creating a plan that best suits the client. As always, be sure to keep client health and goals as the driving force.

Chapter Five: Program Design

Having a personalized exercise program is important for many reasons. Personalized exercise plans allow an individual to set and achieve goals that are relevant to them. By doing this, they increase the likelihood that they will stick to their fitness routine, as opposed to individuals who grow frustrated with routines that do not reach their goals.

Workouts that do not suit them can be set aside in favor of workouts that suit their needs, allowing them to devote more time to what is important to them. Finally, a personalized exercise plan helps people remain accountable. It changes exercise from something that they will do when they get around to it into something they do regularly.

The Optimum Performance Training (OPT) Model

It is important to know the client's goals, exercise tolerance, abilities, and concerns due to previous injuries. A trainer should also keep in mind the fitness assessments to ascertain the best match for the client. Additionally, it can be helpful to know the preferred type of exercise for the client, to increase engagement.

This information allows the trainer to create a training plan, or the specific outlines that will help the client meet their goal. One of the best ways to design programs relies on periodization. This is an approach to designing programs that splits the plan into distinct cycles to improve adaptability and response.

Training Cycles

The macrocycle is the long-term plan for the year. This plan can change from month to month, but will always refer to the client's goals.

The mesocycle is the monthly plan, which divides the training into monthly cycles, with a specific training schedule.

The microcycle is the weekly plan, which outlines the specific workouts to be accomplished within the week.

Linear periodization

Linear periodization involves increasing the intensity while decreasing the volume. Nonlinear periodization involves changing the volume, intensity, and type of exercise to bring about differences on a daily or weekly basis. Nonlinear is preferred, as it keeps workouts from becoming a boring routine.

NASM developed the OPT model as a way to systematically plan a periodized program. Using this method, a client can improve many physical abilities. There are three levels to work through. Depending on the needs of the client, they can stop on level 1, move to levels 2 and 3, or step down to the previous level.

Level 1: Stabilization

The goal of this level is to develop proper movement patterns and to improve movement and stability throughout the entire kinetic chain. This base level will provide the foundation for all exercises moving forward.

At this level, clients are prepared for training by developing the proper movement patterns, gaining exercise skills and knowledge of various machines, correcting muscle imbalances, improving activation of the core and stabilization of the spine and pelvis, enhancing balance and coordination, preparing muscles and joints for increased demand, improving cardiorespiratory endurance, and growing in confidence.

There is only one phase at this level: stabilization endurance training. In this phase, the client prepares for future exercise through these movements: squat, hip hinge, pulling, pushing, pressing, and multiplanar movement.

Level 2: Strength

This level focuses on:

- Increasing the ability of the core musculature to stabilize the pelvis and spine under heavier loads through greater ranges of motion
- Increasing the load-bearing capabilities of muscles, tendons, ligaments, and joints
- Increasing the volume of training
- Increasing metabolic demand by taxing the phosphocreatine (ATP-PC) and glycolytic energy systems to induce cellular changes in muscle
- Increasing recruitment of more motor units to overcome an external load (maximal strength)

Within the strength level, there are three distinct phases.

1. Strength endurance training, which promotes stabilization endurance, hypertrophy, and strength. During this phase, supersets are commonly used, with the first focusing on strength and the second on stability.
2. Muscular development training, which promotes muscle growth. During this phase, there is a focus on training with a high volume.
3. Maximal strength training, which requires the client to lift more closely to maximum capacity.

Level 3: Power

This stage focuses on the speed of muscular contractions. During this phase, the client will train with heavy loads of around 85 – 100 percent intensity and in the 1 – 5 rep ranges.

So, in total, there are three levels and five phases for a client to progress through. Each daily workout should come in six parts.

1. **The warm-up**, which can include self-myofascial release techniques, static stretching, and optimal dynamic stretching, along with some light cardio.
2. **Activation**, which will combine form and balance exercises to further engage the body.
3. **Skill development**, which includes polymetric and SAQ exercises.
4. **Resistance training**, which should focus on movement patterns.
5. **Client's choice of activity** to keep up the enjoyment
6. **Cool down**. Do the warm-up in reverse.

The OPT model is a straightforward and effective way to design an exercise program. Using this phase-by-phase method allows the client to notice and appreciate their progress. The periodization also helps the client to stay engaged with the routine and work a balance of muscles. Each phase prepares the client for the one to follow, which prevents the risk of injury and allows the trainer to better understand their abilities.

Introduction to Exercise Modalities

A modality is a specific method used to encourage a different reaction. There are many different modalities in exercise, as we are always searching for more effective ways to train. In this section, we will discuss strength training machines, free weights, cable machines, elastic resistance, kettlebell training, bodyweight training, suspended bodyweight training, sandbags, ViPR, and battle ropes.

When choosing a modality, keep in mind the different risks and rewards of each. Never use a new modality until the client has mastered the basic movement patterns. Use caution when training on an unstable surface. Though balance is an important aspect of the OPT model, the trainer should have a slow and measured approach to introducing balance modalities. Recognize the limitations of fitness apps, as they are not always accurate and do not always exemplify a balanced approach.

Strength Training Machines

These machines are a popular modality, especially for newer clients. The benefits of these machines include ease of use and less intimidation when compared to free weights. They also do not require a spotter and can be used to help those who lack stability to develop strength. However, these machines only train in one plane and in a fixed range of movement. To train functionality, a person must work in all planes of motion.

Free Weights

Free weights, on the other hand, do allow for training in all planes of motion. They are very beneficial for motor learning, muscular coordination, and performance. However, there is a higher risk of injury, especially for beginners, when compared to strength training machines.

Cable Machines

These machines offer a good hybrid between free weights and strength training machines, as they allow for freer movement like free weights and security like strength training machines. They help develop stability, muscular endurance, and hypertrophy. However, it is important to align the resistance angle with the line of pull to increase the effectiveness of the machine.

Elastic training

This comes with many benefits. It is less expensive than other modalities and can improve coordination, muscular endurance, and joint stability. It also allows for movement across many planes and can be adjusted to make the line of pull higher or lower. The only drawback is that elastic loses its resistance over time, rather than providing a constant.

Kettlebell Training

Kettlebell training is performed with flat-bottomed iron balls with handles on top. It increases athleticism, coordination, balance, physical stamina, total body conditioning, core stability, and grip strength. However, it has similar drawbacks to free weights, and the lower center of gravity can take time to get used to.

Bodyweight Exercises

These exercises use a person's weight to provide resistance. To provide further resistance, weight can be added to the body. This modality allows for movement in all planes and a greater sense of kinesthetic awareness.

Suspended Bodyweight Training

This is a new way to use body weight as resistance using rope and webbing. Benefits include increased core muscle activation, low spinal compression, increased balance, and increased joint mobility.

Sandbags

Sandbags are designed to be carried, lifted, thrown, and pulled. Unlike typical weights, sandbags can be adjusted by adding or removing sand. They also have a shifting weight that challenges balance and stability. They also provide a variety of grips and provide a functional training experience, as sandbags more closely mirror the kind of loads a person may need to carry outside of exercise.

ViPR

This is a modality that focuses on load movement training. It is a rubber tube with handles and openings at both ends. It helps improve balance, stability, and strength and can be used for common training forms.

Battle Ropes

These heavy ropes can be used for a high-intensity, full-body workout. The focus is on cardiovascular training but is also beneficial for resistance training. They have the benefit of being low-impact, as it does very little damage to the joints.

Proprioceptive modalities

These focus on the ability to sense the body's position and movement of the limbs, an ability that is essential for balance. There are many options for proprioceptive modalities, each with strengths and weaknesses and each designed for use in a particular set of exercises. Here are the three main types commonly used.

- **Stability balls** are large round balls that increase the demand for stability during exercise and help with posture during squatting.
- **Bosu balls** are a hemisphere with half a ball attached to a plastic surface. It can train balance and proprioception with certain exercises.
- **Terra-core** has an inflated top and a hard bottom, designed for use in many exercises. It is commonly used in group settings or classes.

Keeping Track of Fitness

Fitness trackers are another useful tool for training, as they are capable of monitoring, and keeping people accountable, and can be useful for medical reasons. They are usually fairly accurate, but may not be perfect. Make sure to verify information obtained from a tracking device.

Fitness and nutrition apps are an easily accessible way to keep track of fitness. They can allow individuals to access information easily, can personalize some aspects of a fitness program, can be used as a log of achievements, and can give reminders. Heart rate monitors are also popular and can be used to keep track of exertion throughout the day.

Chronic Health Conditions and Special Populations

One important group that needs to have increased awareness and access to fitness training is youth, anywhere from ages 6 to 20. The amount of activity performed by this group has been in a steady decline. However, adolescence is an important time for setting up the habits that will continue throughout life. By increasing awareness and access to fitness training for youth, we create more active adults.

Adolescents need at least sixty minutes of vigorous activity daily. However, only around 25% of youth will meet this guideline.

Children should spend time in activity, but it is important to note that they have physiological differences. When compared to adults, children are not as efficient at taking in oxygen, so, during Submax exercise, they will frequently exercise at their peak oxygen intake. They also do not produce enough glycolytic enzymes to sustain much high-intensity exercise. Children also have a delayed thermoregulatory system and a limited ability to sweat. It is important to keep these things in mind because it informs what children can accomplish.

Resistance training is safe for children and adolescents. They should use 1-2 repetitions at 40-70% intensity for best results. Only mature adolescents should use a progression of exercise programs.

Older adults are another important group to have increased awareness of exercise. There are differences in response to exercise between older and younger adults, but it is equally important to both. For older adults, exercise helps maintain good health during the decline of physiologic function.

For older adults, a fitness professional can be extremely helpful. To avoid injury, progress must be slow and monitored. A physical trainer can help an older adult approach exercise slowly, establishing postural support before free-standing exercise is attempted.

Another population to be aware of is those who struggle with weight management, as regular physical activity and exercise are some of the most important factors in weight loss. Regular exercise has even been shown to have a significant effect on the treatment and prevention of type 2 diabetes. Exercise controls the amount of glucose in the body, and allows the body to use energy during activity.

Prevention of coronary heart disease is also an important benefit of exercise. This is a leading cause of death in both men and women, stemming from plaque formation in the heart. Exercise reduces heart failure symptoms and can even lower the risk of mortality. When training individuals with heart conditions, always progress only with their physician's advice and ensure that the exercise does not put unnecessary strain on the heart.

For individuals with osteoporosis, which is a condition in which the bones become porous and break easily, exercise is essential for rebuilding or maintaining bone density. Exercise should combine resistance training with flexibility, core, and balance training.

Physical trainers should also know the difference between rheumatoid arthritis and osteoarthritis. Rheumatoid arthritis is a condition in which the body's immune system attacks the joints, weakening them. Osteoarthritis is caused by simple mechanical wear and tear on joints. Be aware that stiffness, intense pain, and swelling in the joints may be signs of an acute rheumatoid arthritis exacerbation. Always monitor the progress of clients who have arthritis to understand the effect of the exercise program on their joint pain.

Exercise is also important for clients who are recovering from cancer. Cancer treatments can cause clients to feel weakened, fatigued, and physically unfit. Regular exercise can help these clients to rebuild strength and stamina. It improves the quality of life as clients regain normalcy and control over their bodies.

Pregnant clients should not be discouraged from exercise. Studies have repeatedly shown that there are very beneficial effects of exercise for both the mother and the baby. Some exercises that may be helpful are low-impact step aerobics and resistance training at light loads.

For those with chronic lung disease, helpful exercises can include those meant to strengthen cardiorespiratory health. Activities like a treadmill, stationary bike, steppers, and elliptical trainers are beneficial. For resistance training, use one set in a PHA system.

For clients with Peripheral Arterial Disease (PAD), the primary limiting factor is leg pain. When designing an exercise program for these individuals, use treadmills, stair-steppers, and ellipticals in conjunction with a circuit-training format for resistance.

It is very important to create personalized exercise plans for clients to help them achieve their goals and follow through. One of the best ways to create this personalized exercise plan is with the OPT, which helps physical trainers periodize and help their clients succeed. Being prepared to tailor exercise plans to anyone, including special populations, will make you a better physical trainer.

Chapter Summary

- Personalized exercise programs are the best way to help a client set and achieve their goals.
- The OPT model provides a systematic approach to planning the program, with distinct levels and phases.
- Exercise is crucial for all people, including those in special populations.

In the next chapter, you will learn how to incorporate the OPT model and training instruction. This will allow you to guarantee that your fitness program can help the client reach their goals.

Chapter Six: Exercise Technique and Training Instruction

The cornerstone of effective fitness programs is correctly and safely implementing a variety of training concepts. This helps clients achieve their goals while staying safe. There are many different training concepts that we will discuss in the upcoming chapter.

Integrated Training and the OPT Model

One training concept is called integrated training, which puts together all the forms of exercise, including flexibility, cardiorespiratory, balance, core, plyometrics, speed, agility, quickness, and resistance training. This creates a well-balanced approach.

Before intensifying a training program, the body needs a solid foundation in fitness. Clients should not be immediately placed in the most intense workouts, as that will lead to self-doubt or even injury. Instead, the physical trainer must help the client progress reasonably. Giving the body time to adjust before moving forward helps it to become more adaptable and eventually stronger.

In whatever training concept is used, the physical trainer must know and be able to demonstrate the fundamental movement patterns. Mastering these movements reduces the risk of injury and improves the effectiveness of an exercise. These basic movements include: squatting, hip hinge, pulling motions, pushing motions, and vertical pressing. These movements help with coordination and athleticism.

In addition to correct movement, the client must achieve correct posture. Without this, there is an added concern of injury. Therefore, one of the purposes of exercise is to maintain an ideal posture.

Range of Movement (ROM)

Another helpful aspect is training for a good ROM. For the health of muscles and joints, exercises should be performed in a full range of movement. Exercises should be planned in such a way that the client moves through the sagittal, transverse, and frontal planes.

Acute variables of training will change as the client progresses. This is vital, as the client will change over time, and the variables need to match the person that they become.

Goals of the 5 Phases of the OPT Model

Chapter 5 discussed that the NASM's OPT model is based on evidence and split into three levels and five phases. The three levels are **Stabilization, Strength**, and **Power.** The goals of the five phases are:

1. **Stabilization endurance training:** preparing muscles, tendons, ligaments, and joints for the increased demands of physical training.
2. **Strength endurance training:** promotes stabilization endurance, hypertrophy, and strength.
3. **Muscular development training:** increases growth of the muscles.
4. **Maximal strength training:** increases the muscle force-generating capacity.
5. **Power training:** increases the rate of force production.

Flexibility Training Concepts

Flexibility training allows the body to move unhindered. The purpose of this type of training is to increase the range of motion for the joints and improve the extensibility of tissues.

Flexibility is the ability to stretch soft tissue, allowing for a joint's full range of movement. Good flexibility allows for a full range of movement and mobility. Poor flexibility can negatively impact movement patterns as the body tries to complete the movement with the least amount of resistance.

Some terms and definitions to be aware of include:

- **The kinetic chain** refers to the human movement system, which is comprised of the nervous, muscular, and skeletal systems. It contains both the upper and lower kinetic chains.
- **Muscle imbalances** are places in which there are alterations in the lengths of muscle around a joint. They can be either over or under-active. Muscle imbalances create poor posture, which leads to improper movement and potential injuries.
- **Synergistic dominance** takes place when the synergist muscles take over due to the agonist muscle being weakened. This will cause movement pattern dysfunction as the muscles attempt to compensate.
- **Neuromuscular efficiency** is the ability of the nervous system to utilize the correct muscles to complete a task. A lack of neuromuscular efficiency can cause a muscle imbalance. Flexibility training can lead to increased neuromuscular coordination. Therefore, the more a person trains for flexibility, the more efficient their neuromuscular system.
- **Altered joint motion** can cause pain and a decreased range of movement. Poor movement efficiency means that a person does not have sufficient mobility, strength, or flexibility to complete a movement correctly.

Pattern Overload and Cumulative Injury Cycle

Performing a movement pattern correctly can assist in creating pathways in the brain that direct it on how best to act. However, practicing the movement incorrectly due to a muscle imbalance will cause the brain to create the habit of moving poorly as well. Whether used correctly or incorrectly, pattern overload (repeating the same movement patterns) will set a person up to continue performing them in that way.

Similarly, a cumulative injury cycle takes place when one injury leads to another injury. This cycle takes place when tissue trauma causes inflammation, which causes muscle spasms, which causes adhesion, which leads to alterations in neuromuscular control and muscle imbalances, and the cycle continues until something intervenes.

Types of Flexibility Training

There are three main types of flexibility training.

1. **Self-myofascial techniques** puts force on a knot, keeping the force applied to it until the knot releases.
2. **Static stretching** takes the muscle through a passive point of tension and holds the stretch.
3. **Active stretching** uses both agonist and synergist muscles to move a joint through its full range of movement.

To keep the client from causing injury, the physical trainer must be able to inform them of the correct technique.

Cardiorespiratory Fitness Training

This improves the efficiency of the cardiovascular system, ensuring that the muscles receive enough oxygen during exercise. Some benefits of this type of exercise include:

- Decreased heart rate and blood pressure
- Increased stroke volume and cardiac output
- Improved gas exchange and oxygen uptake
- Decreased blood flow and airway resistance
- Improved oxygen uptake
- Increased blood volume

- Improved blood lipid profile
- Improved blood flow back to the heart

Cardiorespiratory training builds the ability of the cardiorespiratory system in its function of giving the muscles oxygen during sustained activity. There are seven key components of physical fitness to keep in mind when approaching cardiorespiratory training, known as FITTE-VP. Using these seven components will help you plan for the individual.

1. **Frequency** refers to the number of training periods within a set amount of time. For instance, a person may choose to work out three days a week. The recommended level of frequency is 150 minutes of high-intensity aerobics done five times a week.
2. **Intensity** is the level of demand an activity puts on the body. Moderate intensity is when the individual is working hard, with a higher-than-normal pulse and respiration rates, but without breathlessness or exhaustion. This can be monitored through MET, ratings of perceived exertion, or the talk test.
3. **Time** refers to the length of time a person is investing in an activity. Adults should get at least two hours and thirty minutes of moderate activity and fifteen minutes of vigorous activity every week.
4. **Type** is the mode of activity chosen. This can be anything from gym-based activities, like weight training, to group activities, like a Zumba class. It can even include activity that is part of daily life.
5. **Enjoyment** is the level of pleasure that comes from engaging in the activity. Although this is often overlooked, how much a client enjoys an activity dictates how likely they are to continue with their exercise programs.
6. **Volume** refers to the total amount of work within a timeframe. Generally measured by the week, this refers to the number of sets, the weight lifted, the distance ran, etc.
7. **Progression** is the amount that the program changes to match the progress of the client. Ideally, progression means that a person moves toward their goals so it is always a challenge.

Exercise training sessions should include the four training zones:

1. Heart rate max between 65% and 75% with low intensity overall. Examples include yoga, walking, and light jogging.

2. Heart rate max between 76% and 85% with moderate intensity overall. Examples include kickboxing and dance classes.
3. Heart rate max between 86% and 95% with high-intensity interval training. This includes activities like sprinting.
4. Heart rate max is at or around maximum with at or close to maximum intensity. An example of this would be sprinting, but at maximum speed.

There are also a total of five stages in an exercise training session:

1. The goal of stage one is to develop cardiovascular fitness to avoid exhaustion. In this stage, clients should exercise at a maximum heart rate of 65% to 75%, or to the point that talking for 10-20 seconds becomes challenging. Examples of this stage are warm-ups, cool-downs, or a thirty-minute workout in zone one.
2. The goal of stage two is to introduce clients to a higher intensity through interval training. In this stage, clients should train in intervals ranging from a maximum heart rate of 65% to 85%, or between the point that talking is challenging to the point that it is difficult. An example of this stage is moving between zone one and zone two. It can be helpful to start with a higher ratio of lower intensity and work to an equal ratio of low to high intensity.
3. This stage is designed for clients who have progressed to the point that they have a moderately high cardiorespiratory fitness level. In this stage, clients should train in intervals ranging from 65% to 95% of maximum heart rate, or moving between the points where talking is difficult to impossible. An example of this stage is warming up in zone one, then increasing the workload every sixty seconds until reaching zone three. After a minute in zone three, go back to zone two, and repeat for the desired number of intervals.
4. This stage is meant to briefly overload the body. In this stage, clients should warm up in zone one, then increase the workload every sixty seconds until reaching zone four. After performing at zone four for ten seconds, decrease the workload back to zone one. This can be repeated as many times as the heart is able to decrease to a normal heart rate. If the heart rate does not drop to an appropriate level, remain in zone one for the duration of the workout.

5. This stage is for athletes. It focuses on the drills that improve linear, multidirectional, and sport-specific activities.

It is important to use caution when performing cardiorespiratory exercises. If the client has poor posture while standing or doing some motions, the trainer must correct the alignment to minimize the risk of injury. Look for a forward head and rounded shoulders, anterior pelvic tilt, adducted and internally rotated knees, and pronated feet.

Core Training Concepts

The core is also known as the lumbo-pelvic-hip complex, which can be divided into local muscles and global muscles.

- **Local muscles** attach on or near vertebrae and may have short attachments between vertebrae. They will be mainly type one muscle fibers.
- **Global muscles** are positioned outside the trunk, acting to move the trunk, transferring loads from upper to lower, and giving stability to the spine.

Benefits of core training include

- Enhanced posture
- Better spinal health
- Better bodily function for daily movement
- Increased balance and stabilization
- Better coordination throughout the kinetic chain
- Minimized back pain
- Improved movements and power

Designing a core training program

Exercises should aim to develop stability, endurance, strength, and power through this critical sequence:

1. **Intervertebral stability** helps with the stabilization of individual spinal

segments. Exercises should focus on stabilizing the spine and pelvis without gross movement of the trunk. Examples include planks, side planks, and floor-prone cobra positions.

2. **Lumbopelvic stability** helps with the stabilization of the lumbo-pelvic-hip complex. Exercises should consist of dynamic concentric and eccentric movements in a full range of motion. Examples include back extensions, side bends, and trunk rotations.

3. **Movement efficiency** helps with improved movement quality and force output. Exercises should improve the rate of producing force and efficiency of movement, aiming to stabilize and generate force at functional speeds. Examples include rotation chest passes, overhead crunch throws, and soccer throws.

This sequence is important because it helps the clients progress safely, as they establish a foundation before introducing strength and power movements.

Abnormal curvatures

Lordotic curves are inward curves of the cervical and lumbar spine. Kyphotic curves are outward curves of the thoracic and sacral spine. Scoliosis is an abnormal spinal curve from side to side. All of these abnormal curves cause a combination of overactive and underactive muscles. Even in people without these conditions, it is important to note which muscles are being over and under-used. For many people, global muscles are strong, but the local muscles are lacking.

Core training becomes especially important because it increases speed, performance, and injury resistance. The proper functioning of the core muscles helps stabilize and correct some of the difficulties created by abnormal curvature.

Balance Training Concepts

Balance training is essential for both general performance and reducing the risk of falls and ankle sprains. It improves:

- Landing mechanics and lower-body muscular strength

- Proprioception and body awareness
- Agility
- Hip and lower extremity muscles by increasing strength
- Balance after injury
- Performance for athletes

Older adults also report an increased ability to participate in daily living and a decrease in disability

To change the level of difficulty in a balance training program, a person can focus on different kinds of balance. Balance can be:

- **Static:** maintaining posture and control in a non-moving position
- **Semi-dynamic:** maintaining posture and control while only the base moves
- **Dynamic:** maintaining posture and control while the center of gravity continuously changes

Keeping balance requires the combination of:

- **Vision:** to see where you are in relation to your surroundings and where body parts are in relation to others.
- **Vestibular sense:** to feel a sense of balance and knowledge of body position
- **Somatosensation:** includes vibration, pressure, touch, temperature, pain, balance, and sense of position and movement

As balance training can lead to falls if not adequately prepared, trainers should be aware of the limits of the client and help them progress systematically. Remember that quality is always more important than quantity. The five key checkpoints should be carefully watched.

The variables of exercise can be changed in the surface, visual condition, position of the body, and movement of the body.

Plyometric (Reactive) Training Concepts

Also called reactive or jump training, this is only truly applicable to athletes but can be done with other clients. The purpose of this kind of training is to increase explosive movement. Benefits include:

- Increased bone density
- Improved soft tissue strength
- Improved weight management
- Increased strength and power
- Better muscle contractions and nervous system synchronization
- Improved performance for athletes

The explosive moment that takes place in plyometric training utilizes the stretch-shortening cycle. This is when there is an eccentric contraction to store the energy followed by a concentric contraction to make explosive movement.

To perform explosive plyometric movements, a client should have good core strength, stability of joints, range of motion, and balance. The **integrated performance paradigm** refers to the body's ability to properly decelerate, stabilize, and accelerate in a performance-based task.

There are three distinct phases in a plyometric exercise of the stretch-shortening cycle:

1. **Eccentric phase:** where the energy is stored inside the muscle.
2. **Amortization phase:** where the muscle is stabilized.
3. **Concentric phase:** where the stored energy in the muscle is released.

Plyometric exercises should progress in this order:

1. **Stabilization phase:** These are exercises done with 5-8 repetitions at a steady tempo with a 3-5 second pause while landing on the ground, with up to 90 seconds of rest. These include box jumps or squat jumps with stabilization.
2. **Strength phase:** These are exercises done with 8-10 repetitions at a mid-tempo with up to 60 seconds of rest. These include tuck jumps and squat jumps.

3. **Power phase:** These are exercises done with 8-12 repetitions as quickly as possible with up to 60 seconds of rest. These include single-leg power step-ups and proprioceptive plyometrics.

Plyometric intensity is the distance covered and the amount of effort used by the muscles, connective tissue, and joints. **Volume** is expressed as foot contacts, throws, or catches.

Before progressing to plyometric training, clients must demonstrate good levels of body strength, core strength, and balance. It may also be helpful to analyze a client's training history, age, and injury history. Before progressing, it is important to teach proper landing and rebounding mechanics to decrease the risk of injury.

Resistance Training Concepts

This is an essential part of exercise training for all people. Benefits include

- Increased endurance and power
- Increased strength and muscular hypertrophy
- Improved weight management
- Improved resting heart rate and metabolic rate
- Lower blood pressure
- Improved coordination and athleticism
- Decreased risk of injury

The General Adaptation Syndrome (GAS) model outlines the three stages of stress response:

1. **Alarm reaction:** when a person is overzealous in beginning an exercise program, their body will usually enter this stage. The stress on the body will cause fatigue, joint stiffness, and delayed onset muscle soreness (DOMS) at 6-48 hours following injury or acute stress.
2. **Resistance development:** increased performance and the ability of the body to recruit muscle fibers and distribute blood and oxygen will take place in this stage. This stage will create the desired changes as the body works to adapt to stressors.

3. **Exhaustion:** when too much stress is put on the body, it will lead to exhaustion and distress. This can include stress fractures, ligament sprains, joint pain, and emotional fatigue.

The Specific Adaptations to Imposed Demands (SAID) Principle

SAID looks at the body's reactions and adaptations to training and exercise. The body will adapt to meet the type of exercise done and the muscle groups involved. For instance, a bodybuilder who works solely on the arms will see results in the arms, but not in the legs. Specificity can be described as:

- **Mechanical:** the weight and movement put on the body. For instance, light weights to build endurance.
- **Neuromuscular:** the speed of the contraction and the selection of exercises. For instance, slow, controlled movements to develop stability.
- **Metabolic:** the energy demands placed on the body. For instance, longer sessions of resistance training to build endurance.

Resistance training can cause many different adaptations, so many goals can be reached through this style of training. Some common adaptations are:

- **Stabilization:** the ability of the body to provide adequate levels of joint support to keep proper posture during movement.
- **Muscular endurance:** the ability to produce and maintain force production for a long period.
- **Muscular hypertrophy:** the enlargement of the muscle fibers in response to developing tension levels.
- **Strength:** the ability of the neuromuscular system to produce tension internally.
- **Power:** the ability of the neuromuscular system to make the most force possible in the shortest amount of time.

In resistance training programs, there are also a variety of acute variables that can be manipulated to find the correct amount of stress to put on the body. In resistance training, this includes repetitions, sets, repetition tempo, rest interval, training volume, training frequency, training duration, exercise selection, and intensity.

Many training systems that can be used to structure a resistance training program, including:

- **Warm-up set:** 1-2 sets at lower intensities to prepare the body for more intense exercise.
- **Single set:** one set of each exercise.
- **Multiple set:** multiple sets of each exercise.
- **Pyramid set:** sets with increasing or decreasing weights in each set.
- **Supersets:** two exercises together with very little rest.
- **Complex training:** a complex exercise with a heavy load and following it up immediately with an explosive movement.
- **Drop sets:** the first set to failure, then removing a percentage of that weight to continue the set.
- **Giant set:** four or more consecutive exercises in rotation with very little rest between sets.
- **Rest pause:** a slight pause between reps in a set.
- **Circuit training:** a series of exercises one after the other with very little rest.
- **Peripheral heart action:** circuit training that alternates between upper and lower body exercises.
- **Split routine:** resistance training routine that trains different body parts on separate days.
- **Vertical loading:** strength exercises beginning with the upper body and moving to the lower body.
- **Horizontal loading:** completing all sets for an exercise before moving on to the next exercise.

A physical trainer should ensure the client remains safe by gathering all information on the client that will assist in safety, knowing and maintaining proper equipment setup, never using damaged equipment, utilizing spotting techniques, and monitoring the five kinetic checkpoints.

Programs should begin with a focus on stabilization and muscular endurance.

These training styles should be featured at the start of exercise programs for beginners. This is progressed by decreases in the base of support.

The program should then lead to strength-focused exercise once there are sufficient levels of stability and endurance. The goal will be to train hypertrophy and heavier loads.

Finally, the client may train for power focus. This should use a firm base and will increase the rate of force production.

Speed, Agility, and Quickness (SAQ) Training Concepts

SAQ is training that combines:

- **Speed:** velocity measured by the distance covered divided by the time it is covered. Speed is dependent on both stride rate and stride length.

  o **Stride rate:** number of strides in a certain amount of time or within a certain distance.
  o **Stride length:** the distance covered in one stride.

- **Agility:** the ability to sprint in multiple directions while maintaining postural control.
- **Quickness:** the ability to react to stimuli and change motion as a response.

SAQ is also used mainly for athletes but can be done with other clients. It provides stability in all planes of motion and stimulates muscular, neurological, connective tissue, and cardiovascular fitness adaptations. Benefits include:

- Higher top speed and rate of acceleration/deceleration,
- Faster change of direction
- Improved fitness and response time
- Improved technical skills in the change of direction and sprinting mechanics

One of the important aspects of SAQ is developing the proper running mechanics, as this is one of the basic movement patterns that should be developed to complete many physical activities.

SAQ is beneficial for healthy sedentary adults, those with health limitations, youth, and older adults. It will improve the overall health profile and weight loss, and assist in the performance of recreational activities. For youth, SAQ provides an environment that challenges them and assists them in developing greater neuromuscular capabilities. In older adults, SAQ should focus on the activities needed for daily life but will help with decreases in bone density.

High-intensity interval training with SAQ drills can burn more subcutaneous fat than long-duration, low- and moderate-intensity endurance training. This makes it a valid choice for appropriate non-athletic populations, including weight-loss clients.

Chapter Summary

- The OPT model is made up of three levels, stabilization, strength, and power, with a total of five phases with specific goals.
- Exercises should cover movements in the sagittal, transverse, and frontal planes to improve flexibility.
- Frequency, intensity, time, type, enjoyment, volume, and progression are essential to cardiorespiratory workouts.
- Core training should focus on intervertebral stability, lumbopelvic stability, and movement efficiency.
- Balance training improves landing mechanics, proprioception, and muscle strength.
- Plyometric training enhances explosive movements through the stretch-shortening cycle.
- Resistance training utilizes many variables and training systems to adapt to the needs of the individual.

In the next chapter, you will learn more about the modern state of health and fitness and the personal training profession.

Chapter Seven: Professional Development and Responsibility

There are growing opportunities for employment as a fitness instructor. The market size in the industry has grown by 3.1% annually since 2017. In the United States, there are over 63,049 fitness instructors currently employed, with the large majority being women. Fitness instructors are more likely to work at private companies than education companies. Understanding the current marketplace can help a physical trainer better find their place in the market.

The Modern State of Health and Fitness

NASM's systems and methodologies are safe and effective for clients working toward any fitness goal because they are in line with evidence-based scientific principles. For any fitness professional to attain the highest level of success, the focus needs to be on evidence-based practice. These practices are the conscientious use of the current best evidence when making decisions about client care. This ensures that the client is getting the best possible experience and receiving the best results.

NASM uses the proprietary exercise training approach, the Optimum Performance Training (OPT) model. This model focuses on progression, allowing the client to move logically and safely from one stage to the next. It represents the inclusion of flexibility and mobility training, core strength and stability training, cardiorespiratory training, balance training, plyometric training, SAQ training, and resistance training. Created by Dr. Michael A. Clark, it set out to optimize the "relationship between the athlete and trainer" through integrated functional training.

Common concerns in modern health

A disease is a disorder that negatively affects the structure or function of the body. Diseases can be **chronic**, meaning that they develop slowly and continue or worsen over an extended period, or they can be **acute**, meaning that they develop suddenly and last a short time.

Overweight and obese issues

The terms overweight and obese both refer to a body weight that is greater than the normal or healthy weight, resulting from a person carrying more body fat than normal. Obesity is more severe and can create major health risks. Both overweight and obese people are at increased risk of many serious health conditions, including high blood pressure, diabetes, heart disease, stroke, osteoarthritis, breathing problems, and difficulty with physical function.

Regular exercise can help in weight management. Weight management through physical activity can reduce the risk of health conditions and improve the quality of life.

Heart issues

Cardiovascular disease is the overarching term for many of the problems in the heart and blood vessels, including strokes, heart attacks, heart failure, heart valve problems, and arrhythmias.

Hypertension, or a blood pressure greater than 120/80, is a leading cause of heart disease and stroke. Often this is caused by **atherosclerosis**, which is the process of plaque forming in the arteries.

High cholesterol is another major cause of disease, including cardiovascular disease. LDLs are bad cholesterol and HDLs are good cholesterol. The LDL level should be lower than 100 mg per deciliter.

Regular exercise helps the heart's arteries to dilate more easily, improving the overall blood flow, and can also help improve cholesterol levels. This reduces the effect of cardiovascular disease.

Diabetes

This condition affects the body's ability to metabolize carbohydrates, especially glucose, a simple sugar that is an important energy source. There are two forms of diabetes:

- Type One: This is when the pancreas does not make enough insulin, the hormone that regulates the amount of glucose in the blood. Without this hormone, blood sugar will rise to dangerous levels.
- Type Two: This is when the body produces insulin, but the cells do not use it correctly, creating insulin resistance.

In people with diabetes, regular exercise can increase insulin sensitivity, reduce high blood pressure, and improve cholesterol.

Cancer

This is a disease in which the cells in the body grow abnormally, causing serious damage to the body. There are almost 100 types of cancer, and it can occur in almost any part of the body. Exercise can play an important role in the prevention of some forms of cancer and improve the quality of life for those who are in cancer treatment or recovery.

Chronic Obstructive Pulmonary Disease (COPD)

This disease is an overarching term for many chronic respiratory dysfunctions. These dysfunctions are characterized by breathlessness, limitations in airflow, and accelerated declines in lung function.

Muscular Dysfunction

Depending on the location of a muscular dysfunction, the impacts of this condition can vary. Some common locations for muscular dysfunction include:

- **Foot and ankle:** the most common are ankle sprains (the stretching or tearing of ligaments between the bones of the ankle that occurs when a person turns their ankle) and plantar fasciitis (tissue inflammation on the bottom of the foot connecting the heel bone to toes). Both these injuries limit everyday activities and cause pain.
- **Knee:** the most common are patellar tendonitis (inflammation of the patellar tendon), anterior cruciate ligament tears (a tear or sprain of the anterior cruciate ligament), and medial cruciate ligament tears (a tear or sprain of the medial cruciate ligament).
- **Lumbo-pelvic hip complex (LPHC):** consisting of the lumbar spine, pelvis, abdomen, and hip muscle, connecting the upper and lower halves of the body. Back pain and abnormal spinal curvature can often be traced to a dysfunction in the LPHC.
- **Shoulder dysfunction:** very common as the body ages due to instability in the shoulder joint or impingement of the tissue and bone in the shoulder, known as shoulder impingement syndrome.
- **Head and neck dysfunction:** due to poor posture over a long period, head and neck posture can become abnormal. Forward head posture, often seen with an increase in office work and mobile phone use, is a common concern.

Regular exercise and physical activity have a huge benefit on these musculoskeletal dysfunctions. It can correct posture and help to reduce the risk of injury by strengthening the joints.

Healthcare

It is important to understand the scope of practice for the adjacent allied health professionals, as fitness professionals often act as a bridge between clients and licensed healthcare providers. Certified personal trainers will often have these networked allied health professionals:

- Physical therapists
- Athletic trainers
- Chiropractors
- Registered dietician nutritionists
- Licensed massage therapists

The **scope of practice** refers to everything a professional can do within the boundaries of their job. These rules will vary based on location, so a physical trainer should understand their role and the role of other allied health professionals. Working with other professionals will allow physical trainers to best help their clients by recommending someone who can help with other areas and address health concerns. It is important to network with other professionals to recommend effective people.

For further questions about your scope of practice as a physical trainer, refer to the NASM Code of Professional Conduct. This resource will ensure that the client and the profession are both protected. It will allow you to fully understand and act professionally within your role.

Personal Training Profession

Fitness professionals have several options when establishing a personal training practice with clients, including:

- **Commercial health clubs:** as direct employees of the health club, physical trainers are paid hourly. This is one of the most common options for physical trainers.
- **Independent professional:** this means that the physical trainer can set their pay rates, but also means that they must pay the operational cost.

- **Small-group training:** this can provide a more affordable price point for clients while still allowing physical trainers to be paid well.
- **Online fitness coaching:** there is currently growth in the online training industry, with many people motivated to exercise on their own, but benefiting from the guidance of a trainer.

Selling personal training services is about asking a client to commit to an exercise program. To sell a service, a physical trainer needs to uncover the client's needs and present solutions to improve their health, wellness, and fitness.

The first step to success is offering quality customer service. This fosters a positive relationship between the client and the physical trainer. From that point, the physical trainer can build a rapport with the client, meaning that they demonstrate open communication and trust through personal connections.

Forecasting means calculating how many potential clients a trainer needs to interact with daily to keep a consistent number of clients, and how many clients a person needs to take on to meet their financial goals.

Marketing is promoting a service to communicate the benefits of training to potential clients. This includes the four Ps of marketing:

- **Product:** communicate the benefits of using the product
- **Price:** identifying the competitive price of the service
- **Promote:** finding a way to promote the service
- **Place:** choosing the location or distribution method

Social media has become an effective way to market services and to be found by potential clients. Maintaining a social media presence has become extremely important to growing a fitness business. Other digital marketing efforts, like email campaigns, can also be beneficial to finding clients.

NASM requires physical trainers to receive 2.0 CEUs every two years. Beyond recertification, it can be beneficial for a physical trainer to pursue additional education. This can help them develop skills, serve a wider range of clients, or specialize in niche populations.

Physical training is a growing market, making it a good investment for the future. Prioritizing evidence-based practice will help a physical trainer stand out by helping their clients get the best results. Often, these results can help clients manage or overcome common health concerns, including obesity, heart issues, diabetes, cancer, COPD, and muscular dysfunction. These concerns will not be addressed solely through physical training, however, and a physical trainer should always be prepared to collaborate with healthcare professionals to provide the best care.

Physical trainers have many opportunities across different settings and platforms, but should always keep a focus on building rapport and offering quality customer service. To do so, a physical trainer should work to understand client needs and present solutions. To help their skills improve, it is important to continue seeking further education.

In the past few chapters, you have learned about professional development and responsibility, exercise technique and training instruction, program design, assessments, client relations and behavioral coaching, basic and applied sciences, and nutritional concepts. This wealth of information will not only prepare you for the NASM CPT exam but will also prepare you to be the best possible physical trainer. Having learned these lessons, you are now prepared to test your knowledge in the upcoming practice tests.

If the amount of information seems overwhelming, or if you do not do as well on these practice tests as you would like, the ACE Method will help you succeed. Take time to become aware of the things that cause you anxiety in order to combat them. Taking action against fears and worries will help you excel on these practice exams and the real exam.

Chapter Summary

- The fitness industry continues to expand, offering many employment opportunities for physical trainers.
- Always prioritize evidence-based practice and the OPT model for the best client care.
- Many common health concerns can be managed through exercise.

- Understand the scope of practice, including your own and that of other allied health professionals.
- Utilize customer service and marketing techniques to build your fitness business.

In the next chapter, you will begin assessing your knowledge through practice tests.

Chapter Eight: Practice Test 1

1. The peripheral nervous system contains which two smaller systems?

   A. Somatic and autonomic
   B. Photoreceptor and mechanoreceptor
   C. Fine and motor
   D. Sensation and cognitive

2. Which of the following reabsorbs old and damaged bone tissue?

   A. Osteoblasts
   B. Osteoclasts
   C. Osteocytes
   D. Osteoporosis

3. A client is having difficulty nodding, tilting, and rotating the head. Which one of the regions within the vertebral column is likely the area in which they are experiencing the issue?

   A. Coccygeal region
   B. Sacral region
   C. Thoracic region
   D. Cervical region

4. The hinge joint is capable of what type of movement?

   A. Flexion
   B. Abduction

C. Adduction

D. Circumduction

5.   If a client is concerned about bone strength, a physical trainer will likely recommend which vitamin?

A. Vitamin D

B. Vitamin A

C. Vitamin B12

D. Vitamin E

6.   The sliding filament theory is at work when a person:

A. Moves the carpal bones

B. Compresses the spine while jumping

C. Flexes their bicep

D. Is lying down

7.   When calculating the cardiac output, a physical trainer should:

A. Subtract client's blood pressure from normal blood pressure

B. Multiply stroke volume and heart rate

C. Subtract end-diastolic volume from stroke volume

D. Add the heart rate and respiratory rate

8.   A client has been training for muscular development and has noticed an increase in muscle growth. Which hormone is likely responsible for his growth and recovery?

A. Cortisol

B. Insulin

C. Norepinephrine

D. Testosterone

9.   A potential client complains of frequent acid reflux. How will regular exercise affect their condition?

    A. Exercise will agitate the stomach, worsening symptoms.
    B. Exercise will help maintain a healthy weight, improving symptoms.
    C. Exercise increases hormone production, worsening symptoms.
    D. Exercise will not have a major impact on these symptoms

10.   When a person shrugs, which movement are they performing?

    A. Depression and elevation along the coronal plane.
    B. Depression and elevation along the sagittal plane.
    C. Retraction and protraction along the coronal plane.
    D. Retraction and protraction along the sagittal plane.

11.   Movements that are possible along the transverse plane are:

    A. Abduction, adduction, elevation, and depression
    B. Flexion, extension, dorsiflexion, and plantar flexion
    C. Rotation, horizontal abduction, and horizontal adduction
    D. Elevation, depression, and inversion and eversion of the ankle

12.   The split-second transition point where the stored energy in a muscle is released is known as the:

    A. Eccentric phase
    B. Amortization phase
    C. Concentric phase
    D. Isokinetic phase

13.   The first law of thermodynamics explains that:

    A. Energy in a closed system remains constant over time.
    B. Energy is decreased every time it changes forms.
    C. Energy cannot flow from hot to cold, it can only flow from cold to hot.
    D. Energy cannot be created or destroyed, only converted from one form to another.

14. A client wants to be in a state of energy balance, meaning that they want:

    A. To balance energy sources between carbohydrates, fats, and proteins.
    B. To exercise in a way that utilizes all three pathways for metabolism.
    C. To maintain a constant weight by burning the amount of calories they consume.
    D. Perform only steady-state exercises.

15. Which of these types of lipids contain a ring of carbon and hydrogen atoms and can be found in eggs?

    A. Saturated fats
    B. Polyunsaturated fats
    C. Monounsaturated fats
    D. Sterols

16. Personal trainers can:

    A. Provide nutritional counseling, but not meal plans or medical nutrition therapy.
    B. Provide general, credible advice.
    C. Provide meal plans, but only if approached by the client.
    D. Provide the same services as a registered dietician.

17. When there is too much glucose in the bloodstream, the body will convert some of this to

    A. Insulin
    B. Triglycerides
    C. Glycogen
    D. Amino acids

18. Diet supplements can:

    A. Replace a meal, when used in moderation.
    B. Add key nutrients that may be lacking in a diet.
    C. Be more effective when taken at dosages above the UL.

D. Be prescribed to a client by a physical trainer.

19. The two types of motivation are:

    A. External and internal
    B. Personal and societal
    C. Primary and secondary
    D. Phase one and phase two

20. Social support includes:

    A. Informational, physical, empathetic, and mental
    B. Emotional, physical, mental, and spiritual
    C. Physical, mental, emotional, and social
    D. Instrumental, emotional, informational, and companionship

21. How does professionalism help you in the relationship with your client?

    A. Demonstrates that you are a good friend
    B. Demonstrates that you have knowledge and expertise
    C. Demonstrates that you are highly athletic
    D. Demonstrates that you are a good listener

22. A client reports that one of their major obstacles to exercise is a lack of time. How is this concern best addressed?

    A. Help the client address their approach to time management.
    B. Suggest they return to exercise when their schedule is more relaxed.
    C. Tell the client to prioritize exercise over other commitments.
    D. Recommend the client exercise more to help relieve stress from other commitments.

23. Which of the following is one of the psychological benefits of exercise?

    A. Provides a solution to mental illnesses
    B. Reduces symptoms of anxiety and stress
    C. Increases healthy competition
    D. Improves relationships

24.   Self-efficacy refers to:

   A. A person's confidence in their ability to be effective in workout routines.
   B. A person's confidence in their ability to rely on themselves rather than other people.
   C. A person's confidence in their ability to control their behavior, motivation, and performance.
   D. A person's confidence in their ability to use their body to its fullest potential.

25.   In the action stage a person:

   A. Plans to exercise within the next six months.
   B. Has been exercising for less than six months.
   C. Has been exercising for more than six months.
   D. Has been exercising sporadically for less than six months.

26.   Motivational interviewing is used to:

   A. Enhance internal motivation
   B. Determine the client's motivation
   C. Create motivation for the client
   D. Shift client from internal to external motivation

27.   A client is looking to set a weightlifting goal. Which of these goals is a SMART goal?

   A. By the end of the week, I want to bench press double my current maximum.
   B. I want to increase my maximum deadlift by 10 kilograms within six months.
   C. Within the next six months, I want to have better form.
   D. I want to decrease my mile time by ten seconds by the end of the month.

28.   What does SMART goal stand for?

   A. Strategic, Manageable, Actionable, Rewarding, Timeless.

B. Sensible, Meaningful, Ambitious, Results-oriented, Tangible.

C. Specific, Measurable, Achievable, Relevant, and Time-bound.

D. Structured, Measured, Appropriate, Realistic, Timely.

29.   For the best outcome, a client should

A. Determine several short-term goals to create their long-term goal.

B. Determine long-term goals and set smaller goals to help progress to that point.

C. Rely on the physical trainer to set their goals based on the results of assessment.

D. Wait to set goals until they have a basic understanding of exercise, about six weeks in.

30.   Using BCT strategies, physical trainers can help their clients:

A. Become experts in mental health.

B. Communicate effectively.

C. Find support groups.

D. Engage in positive self-talk.

31.   What is social physique anxiety, and how can it be addressed by the physical trainer?

A. Social physique anxiety is the fear of social interactions during exercise. To remedy this, a physical trainer can encourage the client to train outside the gym or other public spaces.

B. Social physique anxiety is the fear of embarrassment in front of exercise groups. To remedy this, a physical trainer can encourage the client to train alone and expose themselves to group exercise over time.

C. Social physique anxiety is the anxiety related to appearance during exercise. To remedy this, a physical trainer can empathize with the client's fears and promote positive body image.

D. Social physique anxiety is anxiety related to performance in front of others. To remedy this, a physical trainer can ask the client to rely on their support groups for words of encouragement.

32. If a client is pursuing the goal of health through exercise, they will need to understand that:

    A. There are trade-offs between pursuing different goals. With their goal, health will have priority over physical appearance and performance
    B. When they set a goal in one area, it will have an impact on other areas. Health, physical appearance, and performance will be impacted equally.
    C. The OPT method is most beneficial for improving performance. Health can be emphasized, but performance will be most improved.
    D. They have set a goal that relies on external motivation. If they want to improve health, physical appearance, and performance, they need to utilize internal motivation.

33. How can a physical trainer best help a client build self-efficacy?

    A. By challenging the client to design programs on their own.
    B. By helping clients design programs based on their abilities and needs.
    C. By helping clients look beyond their current abilities when designing programs.
    D. By controlling the client's design program with unchanging routines.

34. What is the desired effect of good communication?

    A. The client will have all the information they need for optimal performance.
    B. The client will feel free to ask questions whenever they have concerns.
    C. The client will feel that the trainer listens to and respects their opinion.
    D. The client will feel that the trainer is a good friend they can rely on.

35. What are subjective norms, and how will they impact a client?

    A. Subjective norms are the unspoken rules of the gym culture. They impact the client's feeling of belonging, depending on how well they pick up on these norms.
    B. Subjective norms are the perceptions of others' expectations. They impact the likelihood that a client will continue to exercise.
    C. Subjective norms are the techniques that are common, but not optimal.

They impact the client by demonstrating poor form, which the trainer must correct.

D. Subjective norms are the body types that are displayed in the media. They impact a client's perception of their own body, causing unrealistic goals.

36.   A physical trainer is working with a client who tends to set unrealistic goals. How can the physical trainer best help this client?

A. Set goals for the client to prevent disappointment when they can't reach the goals they set for themselves.
B. Allow the client to set these unrealistic goals so they continue to push themselves, despite not reaching the goal.
C. Help the client distinguish between outcome-focused and progress-focused goals to help them evaluate the kinds of goals they should be setting.
D. Help the client create better motivation sources so they no longer rely on the completion of goals to feel successful.

37.   Heart rate during exercise is a good indicator of:

A. How much exertion is necessary for the individual to perform an exercise.
B. The number of calories burned during exercise.
C. The individual's maximum oxygen consumption.
D. The ideal duration of future exercise.

38.   Blood pressure should not exceed the normal range of:

A. 160/100 mm Hg
B. 100/50 mm Hg
C. 140/90 mm Hg
D. 120/80 mm Hg

39.   Anthropometry is the study of:

A. The heart conditions possible in human beings.
B. The oxygen usage in human beings.

C. The measurement of human beings.

D. The movement of human beings.

40.   Bioelectrical impedance analysis can be affected by:

A. Bone density

B. Hydration levels

C. Thyroid conditions

D. Blood pressure

41.   The higher an individual's VO2 max, the:

A. Greater the oxygen utilization and ability to do work.

B. Lower the oxygen utilization and ability to do work.

C. Greater the level of subcutaneous fat and ability to convert glucose to glycogen.

D. Lower the level of subcutaneous fat and ability to convert glucose to glycogen.

42.   Hydrostatic underwater weighing works because:

A. Electrical output is more effective underwater.

B. Bone, muscle, and connective tissue are denser than fat.

C. Connective tissue floats, whereas bone and muscle sinks.

D. Fat is not water soluble.

43.   The talk test is:

A. The most precise method of testing oxygen utilization.

B. Ineffective due to the informality and inaccuracy of this kind of testing.

C. An informal way of measuring how exercise impacts exertion.

D. Only to be used after the VT1 and VT2 tests

44.   In the VT2 stage, a client is burning primarily:

A. Fat

B. Carbohydrates

C. Glycogen
D. Glucose

45. You notice that a client has flat feet, internally rotated hips, and is bow-legged. You suspect that this client may have:

   A. Lower crossed syndrome.
   B. Upper crossed syndrome.
   C. Pes planus distortion syndrome.
   D. Scoliosis.

46. One of the best exercises to assess posture is:

   A. Downward-facing dog.
   B. Overhead squat.
   C. Push-ups.
   D. Jumping and landing exercises.

47. Vertical and long jump assessments:

   A. Measure max jump and lower body power, and are suitable for some clients.
   B. Measure max jump and lower body power, and are essential for all clients.
   C. Measure speed and performance, and are suitable for some clients.
   D. Measure speed and performance, and are essential for all clients.

48. The pro shuttle assessment is used to assess a client's ability to:

   A. React, accelerate, and sprint.
   B. Perform complicated maneuvers.
   C. Accelerate, decelerate, and have control.
   D. Endure exercise without fatigue.

49.   Assessments work best in this order:

   A. Performance assessments, cardio assessments, postural and movement assessments, physiological and body composition assessments, then health screening.
   B. Cardio assessments, health screening, physiological and body composition assessments, performance assessments, and postural and movement assessments.
   C. Health screening, physiological and body composition assessments, postural and movement assessments, cardio assessments, and performance assessments.
   D. Physiological and body composition assessments, health screening, postural and movement assessments, performance assessments, and cardio assessments.

50.   How many questions on the PAR-Q+ must a client answer yes to for a physical trainer to advise a client to consult a medical professional before beginning a training program?

   A. One
   B. Two
   C. Three
   D. Five

51.   When there is a need for information beyond the PAR-Q+, the physical trainer can collect this information through:

   A. Postural assessments
   B. Health history questionnaire
   C. Heart rate assessments
   D. The PAR-Q2+

52.   To prevent pressure on the vagus nerve, NASM recommends measuring resting heart rate on the:

   A. Radial pulse
   B. Femoral pulse

C. Carotid pulse
D. Popliteal pulse

53. The heart rate at rest will help determine:

    A. How much exertion is necessary for the individual to perform an exercise.
    B. The ideal blood pressure range for the individual client.
    C. The amount of plaque buildup along the arteries.
    D. Progress over time.

54. The body mass index is known for:

    A. Accuracy through the height and weight measurements
    B. Using circumference measurements to measure progression
    C. Taking into account variances in weight
    D. Inaccuracy, though it can be a good starting place for assessment

55. Skinfold measurements are taken in areas of the body with:

    A. A significant amount of fat.
    B. The least amount of fat.
    C. A significant amount of muscle.
    D. The least amount of muscle.

56. Personalized exercise plans allow an individual to:

    A. Make full use of support systems.
    B. Have consistent, unchanging routines.
    C. Rely on a physical trainer to inform the best practice.
    D. Set and achieve goals that are relevant to them.

57. Knowing the preferred type of exercise for the client is:

    A. Important, as it demonstrates what their body needs most.
    B. Unimportant, as it demonstrates what they are already good at.
    C. Important, as it increases engagement.

D. Unimportant, as it will have no impact on their goals.

58.   Periodization improves:

A. Efficiency of exercise sessions.
B. Adaptability and response.
C. External and internal motivation.
D. Performance in athleticism.

59.   When a client and trainer are working together to create a plan that divides training into monthly cycles with a specific schedule, they are working on the:

A. Macrocycle
B. Mesocycle
C. Minicycle
D. Microcycle

60.   Linear periodization is:

A. Preferred, as it keeps workouts from becoming routine. It increases the intensity while decreasing the volume.
B. Not preferred, as it can lead to workouts becoming routine. It decreases the intensity while increasing the volume.
C. Preferred, as it challenges the client across multiple planes of movement. It changes the volume, intensity, and type of exercise.
D. Not preferred, as it does not challenge the client across multiple planes of movement. It changes the volume, intensity, and type of exercise.

61.   When using the OPT model, which of the following is true:

A. The client should continue progressing, and avoid stepping down to a previous level
B. The client can move to a previous level whenever necessary.
C. Depending on client ability, level one can be skipped.
D. The client should incorporate three levels at once.

62.   The goal of the first level in the OPT model is to:

A. Develop proper movement patterns and improve movement and stability throughout the kinetic chain
B. Assess the client's current abilities, performance, and posture.
C. Develop strength throughout the kinetic chain, with a focus on joints and connective tissue.
D. Assess the client's motivations, support groups, and readiness level, which can be improved through motivational interviewing.

63.   What are the three phases of the second level in the OPT model:

A. Stabilization, movement patterns, and kinetic awareness
B. Gross motor skills, fine motor skills, and advanced motor skills
C. Strength endurance, muscular development, and maximal strength
D. Neurological, muscular, and skeletal

64.   The goal of the second level in the OPT model is to:

A. Develop proper movement patterns and improve movement and stability throughout the kinetic chain
B. Develop motor skills through performance-related exercise
C. Increase core musculature, load-bearing capabilities, and volume of training.
D. Develop the movement system through exercises that strengthen neurological, skeletal, and muscular function.

65.   During the third level of the OPT model, a client will train with:

A. Light loads of around 50-60 percent intensity with 12-15 repetitions
B. Heavy loads of around 85-100 percent intensity with 1-5 repetitions
C. Light loads of around 50-60 percent intensity with 1-5 repetitions
D. Heavy loads of around 85-100 percent intensity with 12-15 repetitions

66.   The warm-up phase can include the following:

A. Form and balance exercises to engage the body

B. The client's choice of activity to begin exercise on a positive note

C. Polymetric and SAQ exercises

D. Self-myofascial release techniques, stretching, and light cardio

67. An exercise modality is a:

A. Specific method used to encourage a different reaction.

B. A variation on an exercise that accommodates disability.

C. Cable or strength training machine.

D. Form of exercise proven to be the most effective.

68. The drawback of strength training machines is their:

A. Inability to train in multiple planes and ranges of movement

B. Long wait times in many gyms

C. Lack of balance training as the client improves strength, causing imbalance

D. Lack of adjustment

69. The shifting weight of a sandbag can improve:

A. Movement patterns throughout the kinetic chain

B. Endurance and reaction time

C. Balance and stability

D. Grip strength and muscle contraction

70. Battle ropes are used for:

A. A low-intensity arm workout

B. A high-intensity arm workout

C. A low-intensity full-body workout

D. A high-intensity full-body workout

71. A client is trying to improve their sense of balance. Which of these modalities will best improve balance?

A. ViPR

B. Suspended bodyweight training
C. Elastic training
D. Bosu balls

72. How much physical activity do adolescents need?

A. 30 minutes of vigorous activity daily
B. 60 minutes of vigorous activity daily
C. 30 minutes of moderate activity daily
D. 60 minutes of moderate activity daily

73. When compared to adults, children are not as effective at:

A. Taking in oxygen
B. Endurance activities
C. Proprioceptive modalities
D. Making good nutrition choices

74. For older adults, the purpose of exercise is to:

A. Maintain a healthy weight despite limited movement ability
B. Improve proprioceptive abilities, reducing the risk of falls
C. Maintain good health during the decline of physiologic function
D. Manage symptoms of common health issues

75. Exercise helps with weight management because it controls the amount of:

A. Calories consumed
B. Glucose in the body
C. Sodium in the bloodstream
D. Cortisol released by the pituitary gland

76. Coronary heart disease stems from:

A. Elevated LDL cholesterol
B. Low blood pressure
C. Lack of sleep in formative years

D. Plaque formation in the heart

77. Individuals with osteoporosis should:

   A. Not exercise, as it increases likelihood of fractures
   B. Not exercise, as elevated heart rate interferes with medications common for this condition
   C. Exercise, as it is essential for maintaining bone density
   D. Exercise, as it will reduce stiffness and swelling in the joints

78. Pregnant individuals should:

   A. Refrain from exercise in the third trimester
   B. Participate in low-impact exercise
   C. Focus on abdominal strength exercise
   D. Be discouraged from all exercise

79. For clients with arthritis:

   A. Always monitor the effect of exercise on joint pain
   B. Refrain from using free weights due to poor grip strength
   C. Advise they refrain from exercise to prevent joint pain
   D. Encourage high-impact exercises for quick results

80. Integrated training refers to:

   A. Putting together all the forms of exercise
   B. Group exercise with participants from many demographics
   C. Performing the same exercise using a variety of modalities
   D. Dynamic movements that involve multiple planes of motion

81. A client would like to begin intensifying their training program. To ensure they are prepared, they will need:

   A. Approval from a healthcare professional
   B. To demonstrate fitness level through performance-based exercise
   C. A solid foundation in fitness

D. Only the motivation to succeed

82.   The fundamental movement patterns are:

A. Flexion, abduction, adduction, and rotation
B. Squatting, lunge, gripping, releasing, and horizontal pressing
C. Squatting, hip flexion, flexing, extending, and lateral pressing
D. Squatting, hip hinge, pulling, pushing, and vertical pressing

83.   A client feels ready to begin intensifying their workout routine. However, they have not yet achieved the correct posture. Why would this be a concern?

A. The ability to accelerate, decelerate, and change direction is negatively impacted by poor posture.
B. Without the correct posture, there is an added concern of injury.
C. Until they have achieved the correct posture, they have not reached the goal of level one.
D. It is not a concern, the client can intensify the routine without achieving the correct posture.

84.   Exercises should be planned in such a way that the client:

A. Moves through the sagittal, transverse, and frontal planes
B. Remains within one plane of movement
C. Demonstrates a full range of movement within one plane of movement
D. Trains one plane of movement in each exercise session

85.   Cardiorespiratory fitness training is designed to:

A. Assess the client's ability before progressing to other types of training.
B. Improve the efficiency of the cardiovascular system
C. Increase stroke volume and cardiac output
D. Increase blood flow and airway resistance

86. To meet the increased demands of physical training, stabilization endurance training:

A. Promotes hypertrophy and strength.
B. Prepares the body to receive heavier loads at higher intensities.
C. Prepares the muscles, tendons, ligaments, and joints for future demands.
D. Increases growth of muscles, the rate of force production, and the muscle force-generating capacity.

87. Muscle imbalance is caused by:

A. Excessive muscle growth
B. Alterations in the lengths of muscles around a joint
C. Genetics and inherited traits
D. Overuse of supplements

88. As a client exercises, you notice that there is a movement pattern dysfunction as their muscles compensate for a weekend agonist muscle. What is the term for this issue?

A. Neuromuscular inefficiency
B. Altered joint motion
C. ROM weakness
D. Synergistic dominance

89. A client's range of movement is limited due to a knot. Which of these types of flexibility training will put direct force on the knot?

A. Self-myofascial techniques
B. ROM techniques
C. Static stretching
D. Dynamic stretching

90. A client would like to begin cardiorespiratory training. As you design their program, which of these components would you keep in mind?

A. Facility, interest, technique, timing, efficiency, variety, and periodization

B. Function, intensity, tempo, target, endurance, volume, and progression

C. Frequency, intensity, time, type, enjoyment, volume, and progression

D. Form, interest, type, technique, effort, variety, and periodization

91. Kickboxing and dance classes are both in the second training zone for cardiorespiratory training. What heart rate range is ideal for these activities?

A. 56-65%

B. 66-75%

C. 76-85%

D. 86-95%

92. In cardiorespiratory exercise, what heart rate range is ideal for clients exercising in stage two?

A. 55-65%

B. 65-75%

C. 65-85%

D. 65-95%

93. What is the difference between local and global muscles?

A. Local muscles are directly responsible for movement, global muscles support the local muscles.

B. Local muscles attach on or near vertebrae, global muscles are positioned outside the trunk.

C. Local muscles support a joint, global muscles are responsible for movement.

D. Local muscles support one section of the body, global muscles support the entire body.

94. Intervertebral stability exercises include:

A. Planks, side planks, and floor-prone cobra positions

B. Back extensions, side bends, and trunk rotations

C. Rotation chest passes, overhead crunch throws, and soccer throws

D. Overhead squats, lunges, and butterfly stretching positions

95.   If an individual has a spine that curves from side to side, they likely have which abnormal curvature?

A. Lordotic curves
B. Kyphotic curves
C. Scoliosis
D. Halitosis

96.   When performing a balance exercise in which only the base moves, an individual improves:

A. Static balance
B. Semi-dynamic balance
C. Dynamic balance
D. Explosive balance

97.   Plyometric training is also referred to as:

A. Explosive training
B. Holistic training
C. Synchronous training
D. Jump training

98.   The concentric phase in the stretch-shortening cycle refers to:

A. The phase in which the brain sends the impulse.
B. The phase in which the energy is stored inside the muscle.
C. The phase in which the muscle is stabilized.
D. The phase in which the stored energy in the muscle is released.

99.   The client is performing exercises within the strength phase of plyometric training, which means they are:

A. Performing 3-5 repetitions at an easy tempo.
B. Performing 5-8 repetitions at a steady tempo.
C. Performing 8-10 repetitions at mid-tempo.
D. Performing 8-12 repetitions as quickly as possible.

100. Before progressing into plyometric training, a physical trainer should teach the client:

    A. Acceleration and deceleration techniques
    B. Landing and rebounding techniques
    C. Ideal intensity for plyometric exercise
    D. The importance of explosive movement

101. In the General Adaptation Syndrome model, exhaustion can lead to:

    A. Stress fractures, ligament sprains, joint pain, and emotional fatigue.
    B. Muscle stiffness, back pain, and poor posture.
    C. Accelerated heart rate and difficulty speaking during the talk test.
    D. Synergistic dominance, lordotic curves, muscle imbalance, and poor posture.

102. The SAID Principle explains that

    A. Speed, acceleration, intensity, and deceleration are dependent on response time in reaction to stimuli.
    B. The body will adapt to meet the type of exercise done and the muscle groups involved.
    C. The type of training used must match the client's stated goals.
    D. A client must progress through the types of training in order of least to most strenuous.

103. If an individual is using heavy weights to build muscle, they are using what kind of specificity?

    A. Metabolic
    B. Muscular
    C. Mechanical
    D. Neuromuscular

104. One adaptation in resistance training is muscular hypertrophy, which means:

   A. The ability to produce and maintain force production for an extended period.
   B. The enlargement of muscle fibers in response to developing tension levels.
   C. The ability of the neuromuscular system to produce tension internally.
   D. The ability of the neuromuscular system to make the most force possible in the shortest time possible.

105. Four or more consecutive exercises in rotation with very little rest between sets are called:

   A. Giant set
   B. Multiple set
   C. Supersets
   D. Rest pause

106. Circuit training that alternates between upper and lower body exercises is called:

   A. Split training
   B. Circuit training
   C. Peripheral heart action
   D. Complex training

107. A client would like to train for a higher top speed and rate of acceleration/deceleration to assist in their athletic performance. The most suitable form of training would be:

   A. Cardiorespiratory fitness training
   B. Plyometric training
   C. Resistance training
   D. SAQ training

108. When compared with low and moderate-intensity endurance training, high-intensity interval training with SAQ drills will burn more:

    A. Subcutaneous fat
    B. Calories
    C. Glycogen
    D. Oxygen

109. The fitness instructor industry:

    A. Is a growing market
    B. Is a shrinking market
    C. Remains the same
    D. Is not relevant

110. NASM's systems are safe and effective for:

    A. Athletes, with an emphasis on performance training
    B. Anyone with a fitness goal, because they are in line with evidence-based principles
    C. Anyone with both internal and external motivations, as motivation is the key to success
    D. Those without pre-existing medical conditions, because current scientific principles advise against exercise for certain demographics

111. To be successful, a physical trainer should focus on:

    A. The client's fitness goals
    B. Athletic ability and performance
    C. Behavioral coaching
    D. Evidence-based practice

112. The OPT model is created to optimize the relationship between:

    A. A client and their support group
    B. A participant and their exercise group
    C. An athlete and a trainer
    D. An individual and exercise

113.   Acute diseases:

    A. Develop slowly and continue over an extended period
    B. Develop suddenly and continue over an extended period
    C. Develop slowly and last a short time
    D. Develop quickly and last a short time

114.   If a client is obese, they should:

    A. Manage diet and nutrition before attempting exercise
    B. Exercise to assist with weight management
    C. Begin extreme dieting for rapid weight loss
    D. Accept the issues that come with carrying additional body fat

115.   Atherosclerosis is the process of:

    A. The heart developing a murmur due to excessive exercise
    B. The heart developing a murmur due to a lack of exercise
    C. Plaque forming along the arteries
    D. Plaque forming along the veins

116.   Which of the following is good cholesterol?

    A. HDLs
    B. LDLs
    C. Both are good cholesterol
    D. Both are bad cholesterol

117.   Type One diabetes:

    A. Prohibits a person from exercise, due to lack of insulin
    B. Is when the body produces insulin, but the cells do not use it effectively
    C. Is when the body does not make enough insulin
    D. Creates insulin resistance due to an excessive amount of insulin in the bloodstream

118.   A client works in an office and spends free time on their mobile phone. Which type of muscular dysfunction are they most at risk of developing?

A. Lumbo-pelvic-hip complex, resulting in spinal curvature
B. Shoulder dysfunction, resulting in shoulder impingement syndrome
C. Knee, resulting in inflammation of the patellar tendon
D. Head and neck dysfunction, resulting in forward head posture

119.   The scope of practice refers to:

A. A professional's network of allied healthcare professionals
B. Everything a professional can do within the boundaries of their job.
C. The specific demographic a professional has received training to assist.
D. The physical area in which a professional works.

120.   The four Ps of marketing are:

A. Product, price, promote, and place.
B. Proximity, perception, population, and persuasion.
C. Productivity, policy, principle, and procedure.
D. Prediction, potential, preparation, and perspiration.

Answer Key

Q.	1	2	3	4	5	6	7	8	9	10	11	12
A.	A	B	D	A	A	C	B	D	B	A	C	B

Q.	13	14	15	16	17	18	19	20	21	22	23	24
A.	D	C	D	B	C	B	A	D	B	A	B	C

Q.	25	26	27	28	29	30	31	32	33	34	35	36
A.	B	A	B	C	B	D	C	A	B	C	B	C

Q.	37	38	39	40	41	42	43	44	45	46	47	48
A.	A	D	C	B	A	B	C	D	C	B	A	C

Q.	49	50	51	52	53	54	55	56	57	58	59	60
A.	C	A	B	A	D	D	A	D	C	B	B	B

Q.	61	62	63	64	65	66	67	68	69	70	71	72
A.	B	A	C	C	B	D	A	A	C	D	D	B

Q.	73	74	75	76	77	78	79	80	81	82	83	84
A.	A	C	B	D	C	B	A	A	C	D	B	A

Q.	85	86	87	88	89	90	91	92	93	94	95	96
A.	B	C	B	D	A	C	C	C	B	A	C	B

Q.	97	98	99	100	101	102	103	104	105	106	107	108
A.	D	D	C	B	A	B	C	B	A	C	D	A

Q.	109	110	111	112	113	114	115	116	117	118	119	120
A.	A	B	D	C	D	B	C	A	C	D	B	A

Answer Explanations

1.   **A. Somatic and automatic.** For more information, refer to "The Nervous System" section in chapter two.

2.   **B. Osteoclasts.** For more information, refer to "The Skeletal System" section in chapter two.

3.   **D. Cervical region.** For more information, refer to the "Vertebral Column" subsection of chapter two.

4.   **A. Flexion.** For more information on how different joints move, refer to "The Synovial Joint" subsection in chapter two.

5.   **A. Vitamin D.** To learn more about how calcium, vitamin D, and protein help build bones, refer to the "Vital Nutrients" subsection in chapter two.

6.   **C. Flexes their bicep.** For an explanation of the sliding filament theory, see the subsection "How Muscles Work" in chapter two.

7.   **B. Multiply stroke volume and heart rate.** For more information, see "The Cardiorespiratory System" section in chapter two.

8.   **D. Testosterone.** Information about these hormones can be found in the "Endocrine System" section in chapter two.

9.   **B. Exercise will help maintain a healthy weight, improving symptoms.** For further information, see "The Digestive System" section in chapter two.

10.   **A. Depression and elevation along the coronal plane.** For more information, see the "Human Movement Science" section of chapter two.

11.   **C. Rotation, horizontal abduction, and horizontal adduction.** For more information, see the "Human Movement Science" section of chapter two.

12.   **B. Amortization phase.** Further information about the stretch-shortening cycle can be found in the "Movement" section of chapter two.

13.   **D. Energy cannot be created or destroyed, only converted from one form to another.** Further information on the first law of thermodynamics can be found in the "Exercise Metabolism and Bioenergetics" section in chapter two.

14.   **C. To maintain a constant weight by burning the amount of calories they consume.** Further information can be found in the "Exercise Metabolism and Bioenergetics" section in chapter two.

15.   **D. Sterols.** For more information, see "Lipids" in chapter two.

16.   **B. Provide general, credible advice.** For more information, see "Nutrition" in chapter two.

17.   **C. Glycogen.** For more information, see the "Exercise Metabolism and Bioenergetics" section in chapter two.

18.   **B. Add key nutrients that may be lacking in a diet.** For more information, see "Supplements" in chapter two.

19.   **A. External and internal.** For more information, see the "Motivation" section in chapter three.

20.   **D. Instrumental, emotional, informational, and companionship.** For more information, see "Social Support" in chapter three.

21.   **B. Demonstrates that you have knowledge and expertise.** For more information, see "Behavioral Coaching" in chapter three.

22.   **A. Help the client address their approach to time management.** For more information about addressing client barriers to exercise, see Chapter Three.

23.   **B. Reduces symptoms of anxiety and stress.** For more information about the psychological benefits of exercise, see "Impact on Mental Health" in Chapter Three.

24. **C. A person's confidence in their ability to control their behavior, motivation, and performance.** See "Designing a Program" in chapter three for a full definition of self-efficacy.

25. **B. Has been exercising for less than six months.** See "Designing a Program" in chapter three for information about the Transtheoretical Model of Behavior Change, which explains these phases of readiness.

26. **A. Enhance internal motivation.** For more information about motivational interviewing, see "Communication with the Client" in Chapter Three.

27. **B. I want to increase my maximum deadlift by 10 kilograms within six months.** For more information, see "Developing a Behavioral Change Technique" in Chapter Three.

28. **C. Specific, Measurable, Achievable, Relevant, and Time-Bound.** For more information, see "Developing a Behavioral Change Technique" in Chapter Three.

29. **B. Determine long-term goals and set smaller goals to help progress to that point.** For more information about helping a client set a goal, see "Developing a Behavioral Change Technique" in Chapter Three.

30. **D. Engage in positive self-talk.** For more information, see "Developing a Behavioral Change Technique" in chapter three.

31. **C. Social physique anxiety is the anxiety related to appearance during exercise.** For more information, see "Social Physique Anxiety" in Chapter Three.

32. **A. There are trade-offs between pursuing different goals. With their goal, health will have priority over physical appearance and performance.** For more information, see the introduction of Chapter Three.

33. **B. By helping the client design programs based on their abilities and needs.** For more information, see "Designing a Program" in chapter three.

34. **C. The client will feel that the trainer listens to and respects their opinion.**

For more information about good communication, see "Communication with the Client" in chapter three.

35.   **B. Subjective norms are the perceptions of others' expectations. They impact the likelihood that a client will continue to exercise.** For more information about subjective norms, see "Designing a Program" in chapter three.

36.   **C. Help the client distinguish between outcome-focused and progress-focused goals to help them evaluate the kinds of goals they should be setting.** For more information, see "Unrealistic Goals" in Chapter Three.

37.   **A. How much exertion is necessary for the individual to perform an exercise.** For more information, see "The Heart" in chapter four.

38.   **D. 120/80 mm Hg.** For more information, see "Blood Pressure" in chapter four.

39.   **C. The measurement of human beings.** For a more complete explanation, see "Anthropometry" in chapter four.

40.   **B. Hydration levels.** For more information, see "Bioelectrical Impedance Analysis" in chapter four.

41.   **A. Greater the oxygen utilization and ability to do work.** For more information, see "VO2 Max Test" in chapter four.

42.   **B. Bone, muscle, and connective tissue are denser than fat.** For more information, see "Hydrostatic Underwater Weighing" in chapter four.

43.   **C. An informal way of measuring how exercise impacts exertion.** For more information, see "The Talk Test" in chapter four.

44.   **D. Glucose.** For more information, see the "Ventilatory Threshold Test" in chapter four.

45.   **C. Pes planus distortion syndrome.** For more information about postural deviations, see "Static Posture" in chapter four.

46. **B. Overhead squat.** For more information, see "Dynamic Posture" in chapter four.

47. **A. Measure max jump and lower body power, and are suitable for some clients.** For more information, see "Push-up and Jump Tests" in chapter four.

48. **C. Accelerate, decelerate, and have control.** For more information, see "The Lower Extremity Functional Test" in chapter four.

49. **C. Health screening, physiological and body composition assessments, postural and movement assessments, cardio assessments, and performance assessments.** For more information, see "Performance Assessments" in chapter four.

50. **A. One.** For more information on the PAR-Q+, see the introduction to chapter four.

51. **B. Health history questionnaire.** For more information, see the introduction to chapter four.

52. **A. Radial pulse.** For more information, see "The Heart" in chapter four.

53. **D. Progress over time.** For more information, see "The Heart" in chapter four.

54. **D. Inaccuracy, though it can be a good starting place for assessment.** For more information about measurement systems, see "Anthropometry" in chapter four.

55. **A. A significant amount of fat.** For more information about skinfold measuring, see "Anthropometry" in chapter four.

56. **D. Set and achieve goals that are relevant for them.** For more information, see the introduction to chapter five.

57. **C. Important, as it increases engagement.** For more information, see

"The Optimum Performance Training (OPT) Model" in chapter five.

58.   **B. Adaptability and response.** For a definition of periodization, see "The Optimum Performance Training (OPT) Model" in chapter five.

59.   **B. Mesocycle.** For more information, see "Training Cycles" in chapter five.

60.   **B. Not preferred, as it can lead to workouts becoming routine. It decreases the intensity while increasing the volume.** For more information, see "Linear Periodization" in chapter five.

61.   **B. The client can move to a previous level whenever necessary.** Information about the OPT model can be found throughout chapter five, but this concept is expanded on in "Linear periodization."

62.   **A. Develop proper movement patterns and improve movement and stability throughout the kinetic chain.** Information on the first level of the OPT model can be found in the "Level 1: Stabilization" subsection in chapter five.

63.   **C. Strength endurance, muscular development, and maximal strength.** For more information, see the "Level 2: Strength" subsection in chapter five.

64.   **C. Increase core musculature, load-bearing capabilities, and volume of training.** For more information, see the "Level 2: Strength" subsection in chapter five.

65.   **B. Heavy loads of around 85-100 percent intensity with 1-5 repetitions.** For more information, see the "Level 3: Power" subsection in chapter five.

66.   **D. Self-myofascial release techniques, stretching, and light cardio.** For more information, see the six parts of a daily workout in chapter five.

67.   **A. Specific method used to encourage a different reaction.** For more information, see "Introduction to Exercise Modalities" in chapter five.

68.   **A. Inability to train in multiple planes and ranges of movement.** For

more information, see "Strength Training Machines" in chapter five.

69. **C. Balance and stability.** For more information, see "Sandbags" in chapter five.

70. **D. A high-intensity full-body workout.** For more information, see "Battle Ropes" in chapter five.

71. **D. Bosu balls.** For more information about balance exercises, see "Proprioceptive Modalities" in chapter five.

72. **B. 60 minutes of vigorous activity daily.** For more information, see "Chronic Health Conditions and Special Populations" in chapter five.

73. **A. Taking in oxygen.** For more information, see "Chronic Health Conditions and Special Populations" in chapter five.

74. **C. Maintain good health during the decline of physiologic function.** For more information, see "Chronic Health Conditions and Special Populations" in chapter five.

75. **B. Glucose in the body.** For more information, see "Chronic Health Conditions and Special Populations" in chapter five.

76. **D. Plaque formation in the heart.** For more information, see "Chronic Health Conditions and Special Populations" in chapter five.

77. **C. Exercise, as it is essential for maintaining bone density.** For more information, see "Chronic Health Conditions and Special Populations" in chapter five.

78. **B. Participate in low-impact exercise.** For more information, see "Chronic Health Conditions and Special Populations" in chapter five.

79. **A. Always monitor the effect of exercise on joint pain.** For more information, see "Chronic Health Conditions and Special Populations" in chapter five.

80.   **A. Putting together all the forms of exercise.** For more information, see "Integrated Training and the OPT Model" in chapter six.

81.   **C. A solid foundation in fitness.** For more information, see "Integrated Training and the OPT Model" in chapter six.

82.   **D. Squatting, hip hinge, pulling, pushing, and vertical pressing.** For more information, see "Integrated Training and the OPT Model" in chapter six.

83.   **B. Without the correct posture, there is an added concern of injury.** For more information, see "Integrated Training and the OPT Model" in chapter six.

84.   **A. Moves through the sagittal, transverse, and frontal planes.** For more information, see "Range of Movement (ROM)" in chapter six.

85.   **B. Improve the efficiency of the cardiovascular system.** For more information, see "Cardiorespiratory Fitness Training" in chapter six.

86.   **C. Prepares the muscles, tendons, ligaments, and joints for future demands.** For more information, see "Goals of the 5 Phases of the OPT Model" in chapter six.

87.   **B. Alterations in the lengths of muscles around a joint.** For more information, see "Flexibility Training Concepts" in chapter six.

88.   **D. Synergistic dominance.** For more information, see "Flexibility Training Concepts" in chapter six.

89.   **A. Self-myofascial techniques.** For more information, see "Types of Flexibility Training" in chapter six.

90.   **C. Frequency, intensity, time, type, enjoyment, volume, and progression.** For more information, see "Cardiorespiratory Fitness Training" in chapter six.

91. **C. 76-85%.** For more information, see "Cardiorespiratory Fitness Training" in chapter six.

92. **C. 65-85%.** For more information, see "Cardiorespiratory Fitness Training" in chapter six.

93. **B. Local muscles attach on or near vertebrae, global muscles are positioned outside the trunk.** For more information on local and global muscles, see "Core Training Concepts" in chapter six.

94. **A. Planks, side planks, and floor-prone cobra positions.** For more information, see the "Designing a core training program" subsection in chapter six.

95. **C. Scoliosis.** For more information, see the "Abnormal Curvatures" subsection in chapter six.

96. **B. Semi-dynamic balance.** For more information, see "Balance Training Concepts" in chapter six.

97. **D. Jump training.** For more information, see "Plyometric (Reactive) Training Concepts" in chapter six.

98. **D. The phase in which the stored energy in the muscle is released.** For more information, see "Plyometric (Reactive) Training Concepts" in chapter six.

99. **C. Performing 8-10 repetitions at mid-tempo.** For more information, see "Plyometric (Reactive) Training Concepts" in chapter six.

100. **B. Landing and rebounding techniques.** For more information, see "Plyometric (Reactive) Training Concepts" in chapter six.

101. **A. Stress fractures, ligament sprains, joint pain, and emotional fatigue.** For more information, see "Resistance Training Concepts" in chapter six.

102. **B. The body will adapt to meet the type of exercise done and the muscle**

groups involved. For more information, see "The Specific Adaptations to Imposed Demands (SAID) Principle" in chapter six.

103.   **C. Mechanical.** For more information, see "The Specific Adaptations to Imposed Demands (SAID) Principle" in chapter six.

104.   **B. The enlargement of muscle fibers in response to developing tension levels.** For more information, see "The Specific Adaptations to Imposed Demands (SAID) Principle" in chapter six.

105.   **A. Giant set.** For more information, see the list of training systems in "The Specific Adaptations to Imposed Demands (SAID) Principle" in chapter six.

106.   **C. Peripheral heart action.** For more information, see the list of training systems in "The Specific Adaptations to Imposed Demands (SAID) Principle" in chapter six.

107.   **D. SAQ Training.** For more information, see "Speed, Agility, and Quickness (SAQ) Training Concepts" in chapter six.

108.   **A. Subcutaneous fat.** For more information, see "Speed, Agility, and Quickness (SAQ) Training Concepts" in chapter six.

109.   **A. Is a growing market.** For more information, see the introduction to chapter seven.

110.   **B. Anyone with a fitness goal, because they are in line with evidence-based principles.** For more information, see "The Modern State of Health and Fitness" in chapter seven.

111.   **D. Evidence-based practice.** For more information, see "The Modern State of Health and Fitness" in chapter seven.

112.   **C. An athlete and a trainer.** For more information, see "The Modern State of Health and Fitness" in chapter seven.

113.   **D. Develop quickly and last a short time.** For more information, see

"Common concerns in modern health" in chapter seven.

114. **B. Exercise to assist with weight management.** For more information, see the "Overweight and obese issues" subsection in chapter seven.

115. **C. Plaque forming in the arteries.** For more information, see the "Heart issues" subsection of chapter seven.

116. **A. HDLs.** For more information, see the "Heart issues" subsection of chapter seven.

117. **C. Is when the body does not make enough insulin.** For more information, see the "Diabetes" subsection in chapter seven.

118. **D. Head and neck dysfunction, resulting in forward head posture.** For more information, see the "Muscular Dysfunction" subsection of chapter seven.

119. **B. Everything a professional can do within the boundaries of their job.** For more information, see the "Healthcare" subsection of chapter seven.

120. **A. Product, price, promote, and place.** For more information, see the "Personal Training Profession" section in chapter seven.

Chapter Nine: Practice Test 2

1.   Which of the following organ systems are of primary concern to a physical trainer?

   A. Respiratory, skeletal, and muscular systems.
   B. Nervous, muscular, skeletal, cardiorespiratory, endocrine, and digestive systems.
   C. Endocrine, integumentary, lymphatic, digestive, urinary, and reproductive systems.
   D. Muscular, digestive, nervous, lymphatic, and respiratory systems.

2.   What type of cells sense light?

   A. Mechanoreceptors.
   B. Photoreceptors
   C. Retinas
   D. Rods

3.   Which electrolyte acts as a calming agent within the nervous system?

   A. Water
   B. Magnesium
   C. Potassium
   D. Sodium

4.   The lower limbs are part of the:

   A. Appendicular skeleton
   B. Sagittal skeleton

C. Axial skeleton

D. Distal skeleton

5.   Intervertebral discs are:

A. Connective tissue that runs alongside vertebrae.

B. Cartilage that runs alongside vertebrae.

C. Cushions between vertebrae, made of cartilage.

D. Cushions between vertebrae, made of connective tissue.

6.   A saddle joint can be found in the:

A. Elbow.

B. Shoulder.

C. Wrist.

D. Thumb.

7.   When the body is not getting enough protein to fuel vital organs through the diet, it will take protein from storage in:

A. Liver.

B. Bones.

C. Muscle.

D. Fat.

8.   Muscles contract when which two proteins work together?

A. Hemoglobin and insulin

B. Amylase and actin

C. Myosin and actin

D. Insulin and acetylcholine

9.   Type one muscle fibers excel at:

A. Endurance

B. Strength

C. Explosive movement

D. Power

10.   What are the responsibilities of the three types of blood vessels?

A. Arteries oxygenate the blood, veins carry blood from the heart, and capillaries carry blood to the heart,
B. Arteries exchange chemicals, veins oxygenate the blood, and capillaries carry blood around the body.
C. Arteries carry blood to the heart, veins carry blood away from the heart, and capillaries oxygenate the blood.
D. Arteries carry blood from the heart, veins carry blood to the heart, and capillaries exchange chemicals.

11.   A resting heart rate is usually between:

A. 50 and 100 beats per minute
B. 60 and 100 beats per minute
C. 60 and 120 beats per minute
D. 70 and 120 beats per minute

12.   Some of the automatic functions controlled by the hypothalamus include:

A. Breathing, heart rate, and involuntary muscle movement.
B. Diffusion of chemicals, gasses, and hormones through the blood.
C. Temperature regulation, hunger, thirst, circadian rhythms, and release of chemicals.
D. Stroke volume, end-diastolic and end-systolic volume, and cardiac output.

13.   Hormones only affect:

A. Cells with receptors that recognize that hormone
B. Organs with receptors that recognize that hormone
C. Cells and organs with receptors that recognize that hormone.
D. Cells and organs, regardless of receptors

14.   The anatomical position is when the body:

A. Is standing with arms outstretched and feet shoulder-width apart.
B. Is standing with arms down and palms facing forward.

C. Is standing with arms at the sides and feet together.

D. Is standing with arms outstretched and feet together.

15. When something is described as being "from top to bottom," it can also be described as:

A. Anterior to posterior

B. Medial to lateral

C. Proximal to distal

D. Superior to inferior

16. How many amino acids can only be attained through diet, and how many can be gained through either diet or manufactured in the body?

A. Nine are essential to get from diet, eleven can be gained through diet or manufactured in the body.

B. Eight are essential to get from diet, eleven can be gained through diet or manufactured in the body.

C. Nine are essential to get from diet, twelve can be gained through diet or manufactured in the body.

D. Eight are essential to get from diet, twelve can be gained through diet or manufactured in the body.

17. Which system is preferred for indicating a carbohydrate's impact on blood sugar levels?

A. Glycemic index

B. Glycemic load

C. Glycogen index

D. Glycogen load

18. What type of sports drink contains fewer sugars and electrolytes than body fluids do, designed to rehydrate without calories?

A. Protein drinks

B. Unflavored drinks

C. Hypertonic drinks

D. Hypotonic drinks

19.   Although a trainer can help an individual achieve a certain look, which factor should inform decisions?

    A. Client's goals and body ideals.
    B. Client's performance and athleticism.
    C. Client's health and safety.
    D. Client's motivations and preferred exercise.

20.   Understanding the factors that influence motivation and habit creation helps a personal trainer:

    A. Create more effective programs and better support their clients
    B. Better understand their own motivations as a trainer
    C. Demonstrate a higher level of education when communicating with a client
    D. Create new motivations for the client

21.   Motivation describes:

    A. Purpose and timeliness of behavior
    B. The social pressures that create behavior
    C. Specificity and relevance of the behavior
    D. Intensity and direction of behavior

22.   If a person has a high level of enthusiasm for a behavior, they are likely to:

    A. Experience burnout as reality will not match their high ideals.
    B. Be willing to invest time, effort, and energy into behavioral change.
    C. Progress at a faster rate than someone with less enthusiasm.
    D. Will be less willing to invest time, effort, and energy into other aspects of their life.

23.   Reevaluating motivations will:

    A. Make the client doubt their original goals
    B. Help keep the goals relevant
    C. Help the client reach maintenance stage

D. Help the client find new motivations

24. When exercise seems inconvenient for the client, which of the following will be most helpful?

    A. Scheduling the client for an exercise group
    B. Holding off on exercise until the client has greater motivation
    C. Helping the client become consistent with their habits
    D. Help the client set new goals

25. What causes ambivalence to exercise and how can it best be solved?

    A. Ambivalence comes from mixed feelings about exercise and can be solved by finding further motivation.
    B. Ambivalence comes from setting unrealistic goals and can be solved by setting more achievable goals.
    C. Ambivalence comes from anxieties about exercise and can be solved by empathizing with the client.
    D. Ambivalence comes from indecisiveness when making goals and can be solved by focusing on the motivators.

26. A person's approach to exercise is strongly influenced by:

    A. Friend's fitness levels
    B. Physical trainer's athleticism
    C. Parent's relationship to exercise
    D. Participants in exercise groups

27. Which of the following accurately describes companionship support?

    A. When someone provides encouragement and empathy.
    B. When someone provides direct action that allows someone to engage in a behavior.
    C. When someone provides accurate information.
    D. When someone engages in the behavior with someone else.

28.   Two benefits of an exercise group are:

A. Sociability and friendship
B. Accountability and comradery
C. Competition and friendship
D. Companionship and information

29.   Self-efficacy can be improved by:

A. Planning and self-monitoring
B. Improved performance
C. Using internal rather than external motivations
D. Utilizing both exercise and diet

30.   Positive affective judgments are:

A. When a person believes that a stimulus is pleasant or enjoyable.
B. When a person believes that a stimulus is unpleasant or unenjoyable.
C. When a person believes that others approve of their behavior.
D. When a person believes that others disapprove of their behavior.

31.   When a client believes others expect them to exercise, they are:

A. More likely to do so.
B. Less likely to do so.
C. Equally likely and unlikely to do so.
D. Unaffected by others' expectations.

32.   The transtheoretical model of behavior change states that people will:

A. Remain either ready or unready to change.
B. Communicate their readiness to change with others.
C. Often make a change before they are ready.
D. Progress to the point of readiness.

33. When someone does not exercise and has no plans to begin exercising, they are in the:

    A. Maintenance stage
    B. Preparation stage
    C. Contemplation stage
    D. Precontemplation stage

34. Active listening involves:

    A. Paying attention to the words used and how they are said.
    B. Paying attention to facial expression, posture, and eye contact.
    C. Asking questions, reflecting, summarizing, affirming, and asking permission.
    D. Using body language to demonstrate that the person speaking has your attention.

35. Which of the following is the correct definition of being specific within a SMART goal?

    A. It should be in alignment with long-term goals.
    B. It leaves no room for ambiguity, answers questions clearly.
    C. It has a deadline.
    D. It should be monitored, with a clear goal.

36. Perceptions and motivations:

    A. Will make it difficult for a client to set realistic goals.
    B. Will help a client begin to exercise and follow through with goals.
    C. Will make it difficult for a client to begin their exercise journey.
    D. Will help a client feel ready to change.

37. The PAR-Q+ test is used to assess which of the following:

    A. Medical conditions that can be improved through exercise.
    B. Medical conditions that prohibit the client from exercising.
    C. Proprioceptive capabilities.

D. Basic health, including heart rate, blood pressure, and respiration rate.

38.   The body mass index, circumference measurement, skinfold measures, bioelectrical impedance analysis, and hydrostatic underwater weighing are all:

A. Pseudoscience, with no true evidence behind them.
B. Ways to noninvasively measure nutritional status and amounts of body fat.
C. Methods of categorizing clients into health status categories.
D. Ways to assess the client's readiness for exercise.

39.   The most accurate test is:

A. Body mass index (BMI)
B. Bioelectrical impedance analysis
C. Talk test
D. Hydrostatic underwater weighing

40.   Circumference measurements are taken at:

A. The waist, neck, chest, hips, thighs, calves, and arms.
B. Areas with the most muscle growth.
C. The wrists, ankles, and elbows.
D. The areas with the largest circumferences.

41.   Circumference measurements provide:

A. Baseline health information.
B. Information about progression over time.
C. An assessment of muscle and fat percentages.
D. Limited variations between people.

42.   In the body mass index, the number 22 would be in which range?

A. Underweight
B. Healthy
C. Overweight

D. Obese

43. Which of the following describes the VT1 stage?

   A. Breathing is easy and the client can hold a conversation.
   B. Breathing is audible but the client can hold a conversation.
   C. Breathing is audible and the client is having difficulty catching their breath.
   D. Breathing is difficult and the client cannot speak.

44. In the VT1 stage, an individual is primarily burning:

   A. Glucose
   B. Carbohydrates
   C. Fat
   D. Glycogen

45. Deviations from the optimal position will cause stress to:

   A. Connective tissues
   B. Muscles
   C. Joints
   D. Bones

46. A forward head and rounded shoulders may be signs of which postural deviation?

   A. Pes planus distortion syndrome
   B. Lower crossed syndrome
   C. Upper crossed syndrome
   D. Scoliosis

47. The kinetic chain checkpoints are at:

   A. Feet, ankles, knees, lumbo-pelvic-hip complex, shoulders, head, and neck.
   B. Head, shoulders, abdomen, wrists, and legs.

C. Neck, chest, waist, hips, thighs, calves, and arms.

D. Ankles, knees, chest, shoulders, elbows, wrists, neck, and head.

48.   When assessing dynamic posture, which of the following should you monitor?

A. Grip strength, hand placement, and stance.

B. Heart rate, blood pressure, VO2 max, and how difficult it is for the client to speak.

C. Feet or knees changing position, back arching, arms falling forward, or difficulty keeping balance.

D. Overall flexibility and joint mobility.

49.   A bench press weight assessment is used to:

A. Measure heart rate.

B. Find a one-rep max.

C. Assess endurance.

D. Monitor stability.

50.   Does reassessment help a client? If so, how?

A. Yes, reassessment demonstrates progress and improvement.

B. Yes, reassessment helps clients create comparisons between themselves and others.

C. No, reassessment demoralizes the client.

D. No, reassessment is a tool for the trainer, it does not help the client.

51.   Why is it important to measure blood pressure in assessments?

A. It measures muscle mass.

B. It demonstrates the level of exertion.

C. It indicates body fat percentage.

D. It can identify health concerns.

52.   A client's blood pressure is 110/70. Is this a cause for concern? If so, why?

    A. Yes, this falls into the high blood pressure range.
    B. No, this is within the healthy blood pressure range.
    C. Yes, this falls into the low blood pressure range.
    D. Retest, it is not possible to have this blood pressure.

53.   Why are anthropometric measurements important in fitness assessment?

    A. Variations in weight, size, and proportion can impact health goals and monitor progress.
    B. Cardiovascular wellness is essential to understanding the exertion that a client is capable of.
    C. Body temperature impacts the ability of the body to perform, especially in endurance exercises.
    D. The amount of oxygen the body can utilize will inform the type of training that will be most beneficial.

54.   When a client has done very well in an overhead squat, they can be further assessed for strength, balance, and coordination through:

    A. Beginning yoga.
    B. An overhead squat with added weight.
    C. A lower extremity functional test.
    D. A single-leg squat.

55.   What does the BMI accomplish?

    A. It assigns a numerical value based on weight and height.
    B. It provides a comprehensive health profile.
    C. It evaluates dietary habits and nutritional status.
    D. It measures cardiovascular fitness and muscular endurance.

56.   Why is a personalized exercise plan beneficial to a client?

    A. It guarantees the results they want.
    B. It increases the likelihood of sticking to a fitness routine.
    C. It requires less effort for the client.

D. It provides comradery and accountability.

57. Which of the following describes a microcycle?

   A. The long-term plan for the year.
   B. The monthly plan.
   C. The weekly outline.
   D. The daily schedule.

58. Periodization helps improve:

   A. Adaptability and response
   B. Comradery and competition
   C. Strength and endurance
   D. Performance-based goals

59. Which are the movements emphasized in the first level of the Optimum Performance Training Model?

   A. Overhead squat, single leg squat, core stability movements, and shifting weight exercises.
   B. Squat, hip hinge, pulling, pushing, pressing, and multiplanar movement.
   C. Running, biking, rowing, and endurance-based exercises.
   D. Bosu balls, stability balls, and terra-core.

60. Correcting muscle imbalances is one of the goals of which level of training in the OPT Model?

   A. Stabilization
   B. Strength
   C. Power
   D. Endurance

61. Increasing the volume of training is one of the goals of which level of training in the OPT model?

   A. Stabilization
   B. Strength

C. Power

D. Endurance

62. Combining form and balance exercises is part of which part of a daily workout?

   A. The warm-up

   B. Activation

   C. Skill development

   D. Resistance training

63. Which is one of the strengths of strength training machines?

   A. Training in multiple planes of movement

   B. Improves balance and stability

   C. Provides a variety of grips

   D. Ease of use and less intimidation

64. Which is one of the drawbacks of free weights?

   A. Limited range of movement

   B. Shifting weight

   C. Higher risk of injury

   D. Lower center of gravity

65. What is the best way to ensure the effectiveness of a cable machine?

   A. Align the resistance angle with the line of pull.

   B. Adjust the starting height to the proper kinetic checkpoint.

   C. Use an unstable base to improve stability.

   D. Ensure that the line of pull is as high as possible.

66. Which of these training modalities is least expensive?

   A. Free weights

   B. Elastic training

   C. Cable machines

   D. Strength training machines

67.   Which of these training modalities is known for being a low-impact full-body workout, with very little damage to the joints?

A. ViPR
B. Sandbags
C. Battle ropes
D. Bodyweight training

68.   What are the benefits of suspended bodyweight training?

A. Better lumbo-pelvic-hip complex training, greater resistance, and functional training.
B. Increased core muscle activation, low spinal compression, increased balance, and better joint mobility.
C. Shifting weight challenges balance and stability, variety of grips, functional training, and ability to be adjusted.
D. Low-impact, full-body workout, improves coordination, and better joint stability.

69.   Stability balls are:

A. Large, round balls that increase the demand for stability and help with posture.
B. Hemisphere with half a ball attached to a plastic surface, designed to train proprioception.
C. Inflated top with hard bottom, commonly used in group settings.
D. Small round balls made in a variety of weights, used to add to body-weight exercises.

70.   Which of the following statements about fitness trackers is true?

A. Should not be used due to frequent inaccuracies.
B. Are a threat to the fitness instructor industry due to their accuracy.
C. Useful for monitoring, accountability, and medical reasons.
D. Are not accessible enough for use in the general population.

71. The fitness levels of youth have:

    A. Been on a steady rise.
    B. Been on a steady decline.
    C. Risen and fallen throughout the past twenty years.
    D. Not been adequately studied

72. What is the result of increasing awareness and access to fitness training for youth?

    A. More teens grow up to resent exercise.
    B. A rise in obesity rates due to decreased interest.
    C. More teens will likely become active adults.
    D. A decline in health and well-being among teens.

73. When working with older adults, physical trainers should:

    A. Establish postural support before attempting free-standing exercise.
    B. Ignore pre-existing medical conditions to focus on exercise.
    C. Focus on building muscle mass and strength, not on flexibility or balance.
    D. Encourage high-intensity, high-impact exercise.

74. Exercise has a significant effect on the treatment and prevention of which of these conditions?

    A. Type 2 diabetes
    B. Anxiety and depression
    C. Allergies
    D. The common cold

75. What is the difference between rheumatoid arthritis and osteoarthritis?

    A. Rheumatoid arthritis is when prolonged exposure to environmental factors leads to joint inflammation, osteoarthritis is caused by repeated movements over time.
    B. Rheumatoid arthritis is caused by repeated movements over time,

osteoarthritis is when prolonged exposure to environmental factors leads to joint inflammation.

C. Rheumatoid arthritis is caused by wear and tear on the joints, osteoarthritis is when the body's immune system attacks joints.

D. Rheumatoid arthritis is when the body's immune system attacks joints, osteoarthritis is caused by mechanical wear and tear on the joints.

76.   Plaque formation in the heart can cause which of the following issues?

A. Asthma and other respiratory issues
B. Coronary heart disease
C. Rheumatoid arthritis
D. Type 2 diabetes

77.   In children and adolescents, what is the best repetition and intensity for resistance training?

A. 1-2 repetitions at 25-40% intensity.
B. 1-2 repetitions at 40-70% intensity.
C. 3-5 repetitions at 25-40% intensity.
D. 3-5 repetitions at 40-70% intensity.

78.   In children, the thermoregulatory system is:

A. Delayed
B. Hyperactive
C. Hypoactive
D. The same as adults

79.   Which of the following may be signs of acute rheumatoid arthritis exacerbation?

A. Loss of stability, shaking, and lightheadedness.
B. Weakness, fatigue, and weakened grip ability.
C. Stiffness, intense pain, and swelling in the joints.
D. Elevated heart rate, blood pressure, and respiration.

80. Being immediately placed in the most intense workouts will likely result in:

A. Better performance over time
B. A greater understanding of the client's abilities
C. Self-doubt and the higher possibility of injury
D. A well-balanced and progressive approach

81. How does progression help a client?

A. Helps the body adapt to new demands.
B. Allows the client time to set goals.
C. Takes away the need for health assessments.
D. Intensifies the program faster.

82. Should a trainer demonstrate the fundamental movement patterns?

A. Yes, it will speed up the training process.
B. Yes, it will help the client understand the proper form.
C. No, it will cause the patient to move unnaturally.
D. No, it will cause the client to attempt things before they are ready.

83. Which phase of the Optimal Performance Training model has a goal of increasing the growth of muscles?

A. Power training
B. Maximal strength training
C. Muscular development training
D. Strength endurance training

84. Power training accomplishes which of the following?

A. Decreased resting heart rate
B. Larger circumference measures
C. Healthier number on the body mass index
D. Increased force production

85.   The purpose of flexibility training is to:

   A. Increase range of motion and extensibility of tissues.
   B. Increase balance, proprioceptive sense, and stability.
   C. Strengthen muscle imbalances and improve muscle imbalances.
   D. Create synergistic dominance and altered joint motion.

86.   The kinetic chains include:

   A. Axial and appendicular chains
   B. Sagittal, transverse, and coronal chains
   C. Anterior and posterior chains
   D. Upper and lower chains

87.   Which is the correct definition of neuromuscular efficiency?

   A. The measurement of how quickly muscle fibers contract and relax.
   B. The amount of strength and power relative to the size of the muscles.
   C. The ability of the nervous system to utilize the correct muscles to complete a task.
   D. The ability to maintain stability and balance through muscles and neurological feedback.

88.   What is a pattern overload?

   A. Repeatedly performing the same exercise or movement.
   B. Using the same workout routine daily for the length of a microcycle.
   C. A set that focuses on form rather than weight or intensity.
   D. Using the same modality for the duration of the exercise program.

89.   When a person has an injury that leads to another, this is known as:

   A. Incorrect movement patterns
   B. Cumulative injury cycle
   C. Dysfunction of the kinetic chain
   D. Muscle imbalance

90. What is static and active stretching?

    A. Static stretching takes the muscle through a passive point of tension and holds the stretch, active stretching uses both agonist and synergist muscles to move a joint through the full range of movement.
    B. Static stretching uses both agonist and synergist muscles to move a joint through the full range of movement, active stretching puts force on a knot until the knot releases.
    C. Static stretching puts force on a knot until the knot releases, active stretching takes the muscle through a passive point of tension and holds the stretch.
    D. Static stretching uses both agonist and synergist muscles to move a joint through the full range of movement, active stretching takes the muscle through a passive point of tension and holds the stretch.

91. Increased blood volume is a benefit of which type of training?

    A. Flexibility training
    B. Cardiorespiratory fitness training
    C. Plyometric training
    D. Resistance training

92. According to FITTE-VP, which of the following refers to the total amount of work within a timeframe?

    A. Frequency
    B. Intensity
    C. Type
    D. Volume

93. What is the goal of stage two in cardiorespiratory training, where clients train in intervals ranging from a maximum heart rate of 65-85%?

    A. To introduce individuals to higher intensity through interval training.
    B. To develop a high level of cardiovascular fitness to avoid exhaustion.
    C. To briefly overload the body.
    D. To develop greater utilization of muscles during exercise.

94.   The responsibility of global muscles is to:

A. Provide secondary support to agonist muscles
B. Give stability to the spine
C. Enhance landing mechanics and lower-body strength
D. Improve soft tissue strength

95.   What is the difference between intervertebral stability and lumbopelvic stability?

A. Intervertebral stability helps with the stabilization of the lumbo-pelvic-hip complex, lumbopelvic stability helps with the stabilization of individual spinal segments.
B. Intervertebral stability helps with the stabilization of individual spinal segments, lumbopelvic stability helps with the stabilization of the lumbo-pelvic-hip complex.
C. Intervertebral stability refers to increasing the compression ability of spinal discs, lumbopelvic stability refers to the strength of muscles in the lumbo-pelvic-hip complex.
D. Intervertebral stability refers to the strength of muscles in the lumbo-pelvic-hip complex, lumbopelvic stability refers to increasing the compression ability of spinal discs.

96.   When should a person begin movement efficiency during a core training program?

A. Before intervertebral stability
B. Before lumbopelvic stability
C. After both intervertebral and lumbopelvic stability
D. Concurrently with intervertebral and lumbopelvic stability

97.   Balance training focuses on:

A. Lower extremity muscles
B. Upper extremity muscles
C. Steady respiration
D. Flexibility

98. Balance training reduces the risk of:

    A. Inactivity in adolescents
    B. Coronary heart disease
    C. Arthritis
    D. Falls

99. Balance requires a combination of:

    A. Posture, position, and a low center of gravity
    B. Vision, vestibular sense, and somatosensation
    C. Landing mechanics, upper-body strength, and agility
    D. Proprioception, body awareness, and muscular endurance

100. Plyometric training is:

    A. Used to increase explosive movement.
    B. Used to increase muscle mass.
    C. A high-intensity training only to be used with athletes.
    D. A low-intensity movement used for injury recovery.

101. The integrated performance paradigm refers to:

    A. Putting together all forms of exercise for maximum performance.
    B. Using multiple forms of training to increase performance.
    C. The body's ability to decelerate, stabilize, and accelerate in a performance-based task.
    D. The body's ability to utilize the stretch-shortening cycle for explosive movement in a performance-based task.

102. Box jumps done with 5-8 repetitions at a steady tempo with a 3-5 second pause while landing on the ground, with up to 90 seconds of rest is representative of which phase of plyometric exercise?

    A. Stabilization
    B. Movement
    C. Strength
    D. Power

103.   According to the General Adaptation Syndrome (GAS) model, what is the correct description of the resistance development stage?

   A. When the body is shocked into a stress response on beginning exercise.
   B. Increased energy demands are placed on the body, leading to higher levels of endurance.
   C. Increased performance and ability to recruit muscle fibers and distribute blood and oxygen.
   D. When too much stress is placed on the body, leading to exhaustion and distress.

104.   Neuromuscular specificity determines:

   A. The weight and movement put on the body.
   B. The speed of contraction and the selection of exercise.
   C. The energy demands placed on the body.
   D. The duration of and recovery time for a specific exercise.

105.   Which of the following is the correct definition of acute variables?

   A. Elements that will change, but will not impact the effect of the exercise.
   B. Decisions made in the program plan that influence the direction of efforts.
   C. An individual's changing ability to respond to exercise.
   D. Elements that can be manipulated to find the correct amount of stress to put on the body.

106.   A resistance training routine that trains different body parts on separate days is called:

   A. Complex training
   B. Split training
   C. Multiple set
   D. Horizontal loading

107. How is speed calculated?

    A. Distance covered divided by the time it is covered.
    B. Stride rate divided by stride length.
    C. Distance covered multiplied by the time it is covered.
    D. Subtract initial position from final position.

108. Which of the following is a direct benefit of Speed, Quickness, and Agility (SAQ) Training?

    A. Improved technical skills in the change of direction and sprinting mechanics.
    B. Improved landing mechanics and lower-body muscular strength.
    C. Enhanced posture, spinal health, and stabilization.
    D. Creates the ability to stretch soft tissue, allowing for a full range of movement.

109. How does the Optimum Performance Training (OPT) model help a client progress?

    A. It creates motivation for the client as they continue their program.
    B. It includes limited training concepts, allowing the client to narrow their scope.
    C. It allows the client to move logically and safely from one stage to the next.
    D. It focuses on the client's performance, giving them concrete goals.

110. Why are evidence-based practices important for a physical trainer?

    A. These practices demonstrate the physical trainer's level of education.
    B. These practices ensure that the client is receiving the best possible experience and the best possible results.
    C. These practices focus on progression, allowing the trainer more time to work with a client.
    D. Using these practices attracts more clients and is a beneficial marketing technique.

111.   Which of the following is the correct definition of a disease?

    A. A disease develops quickly and progressively gets worse over time.
    B. A disease is a temporary inconvenience that will not have long-term consequences.
    C. A disease is a disorder that compromises the body's immune system.
    D. A disease is a disorder that negatively affects the structure or function of the body.

112.   What is the difference between the terms overweight and obese?

    A. Overweight is still within the parameters of a healthy body weight, obese means that a person has an unhealthy amount of extra weight.
    B. Overweight is less severe, obese is more severe, and poses the risk of more serious health risks.
    C. Overweight refers to a higher than normal body weight due to muscle mass, obese refers to a higher than normal body weight due to fat.
    D. Overweight is temporary, obese is permanent.

113.   What are the two types of diabetes?

    A. Type A and Type B
    B. Type 1 and Type 2
    C. Chronic and Acute
    D. Youth and Adult

114.   How does exercise impact diabetes?

    A. Exercise has no impact on diabetes.
    B. Exercise worsens diabetes symptoms.
    C. Exercise creates higher blood pressure.
    D. Exercise can increase insulin sensitivity.

115.   What is hypertension?

    A. A blood pressure greater than 120/80.
    B. A higher than normal level of red blood cells.

C. Irregular heartbeat.
D. Tension in blood vessels.

116. Regular exercise can help:

    A. Blood vessels dilate more easily.
    B. Arteries dilate more easily.
    C. Blood vessels to constrict more easily.
    D. Arteries to constrict more easily.

117. What is the role of exercise in cancer prevention and treatment?

    A. Exercise has no impact on cancer prevention or treatment, as cancer treatment is dependent on only medical intervention.
    B. Exercise has no impact on cancer prevention, but is one of the most valuable tools in speeding up recovery.
    C. Exercise can contribute to preventing some forms of cancer and can improve quality of life during treatment.
    D. Exercise has been shown to contribute to the treatment of most common forms of cancer.

118. What are the most common foot and ankle muscular dysfunctions?

    A. Poor alignment and load distribution.
    B. Foot drop and other nerve compressions.
    C. Ankle sprains and plantar fasciitis.
    D. Arch strain and acquired flatfoot.

119. What system does chronic obstructive pulmonary disease impact?

    A. Cardiovascular
    B. Respiratory
    C. Muscular
    D. Skeletal

120.   Which of the following is a reason for a physical trainer to work with allied health professionals?

   A. To share client information.
   B. To provide a diagnosis.
   C. To address clients' health concerns.
   D. To receive recommendations.

Answer Key

Q.	1	2	3	4	5	6	7	8	9	10	11	12
A.	B	B	C	A	C	D	B	C	A	D	B	C

Q.	13	14	15	16	17	18	19	20	21	22	23	24
A.	C	B	D	A	B	A	D	A	D	B	B	C

Q.	25	26	27	28	29	30	31	32	33	34	35	36
A.	A	C	D	B	A	A	A	D	D	C	B	B

Q.	37	38	39	40	41	42	43	44	45	46	47	48
A.	B	B	D	A	B	B	C	A	C	C	A	C

Q.	49	50	51	52	53	54	55	56	57	58	59	60
A.	B	A	D	B	A	C	A	B	C	A	B	A

Q.	61	62	63	64	65	66	67	68	69	70	71	72
A.	B	B	D	C	A	B	C	B	A	C	B	C

Q.	73	74	75	76	77	78	79	80	81	82	83	84
A.	A	A	D	B	B	A	C	C	A	B	C	D

Q.	85	86	87	88	89	90	91	92	93	94	95	96
A.	A	D	C	A	B	A	B	D	A	B	B	C

Q.	97	98	99	100	101	102	103	104	105	106	107	108
A.	A	D	B	A	C	A	C	B	D	B	A	C

Q.	109	110	111	112	113	114	115	116	117	118	119	120
A.	C	B	D	B	B	D	A	B	C	C	B	C

Answer Explanations

1. **B. Nervous, muscular, skeletal, cardiorespiratory, endocrine, and digestive systems.** For more information, see the introduction to chapter two.

2. **B. Photoreceptors.** For more information, see the "Photoreceptors and Mechanoreceptors" subsection in chapter two.

3. **C. Potassium.** For more information, see the list of electrolytes under "The Structure of the Nervous System" in chapter two.

4. **A. Appendicular.** For more information, see "The Skeletal System" in chapter two.

5. **C. Cushions between vertebrae, made of cartilage.** For more information, see "The Vertebral Column" subsection in chapter two.

6. **D. Thumb.** For more information, see the lists of joints under "The Synovial Joint" in chapter two.

7. **B. Bones.** For more information, see "Vital Nutrients" in chapter two.

8. **C. Myosin and actin.** For more information, see the "How Muscles Work" subsection in chapter two.

9. **A. Endurance.** For more information, see the two types of muscle fibers under the "How Muscles Work" subsection in chapter two.

10. **D. Arteries carry blood from the heart, veins carry blood to the heart, and capillaries exchange chemicals.** For more information, see "The Cardiorespiratory System" in chapter two.

11. **B. 60 and 100 beats per minute.** For more information, see "The Cardiorespiratory System" in chapter two.

12. **C. Temperature regulation, hunger, thirst, circadian rhythms, and release of chemicals.** For more information, see the definition of the hypothalamus in "The Endocrine System" in chapter two.

13.   **C. Cells and organs with receptors that recognize that hormone.** For more information, see the list of important hormones in "The Endocrine System" section of chapter two.

14.   **B. Is standing with arms down and palms facing forward.** For more information, see "Human Movement Science" in chapter two.

15.   **D. Superior to inferior.** For more information, see the list of locations under the "Human Movement Science" section in chapter two.

16.   **A. Nine are essential to get from diet, eleven can be gained through diet or manufactured in the body.** For more information, see "Protein" in chapter two.

17.   **B. Glycemic load.** For more information, see "The Glycemic Index and Glycemic Load" in chapter two.

18.   **A. Hypotonic drinks.** For more information, see "Hydration" in chapter two.

19.   **D. Client's health and safety.** For more information, see the introduction to chapter three.

20.   **A. Create more effective programs and better support their clients.** For more information, see "The Psychology of Exercise" in chapter three.

21.   **D. Intensity and direction of the behavior.** For more information, see "Motivation" in chapter three.

22.   **B. Be willing to invest time, effort, and energy into behavioral change.** For more information, see "Motivation" in chapter three.

23.   **B. Help keep goals relevant.** For more information, see "Motivation" in chapter three.

24.   **C. Helping the client become consistent with their habits.** For more information, see "Inconvenience" in chapter three.

25.   **A. Ambivalence comes from mixed feelings about exercise and can be solved by finding further motivation.** For more information, see "Ambivalence" in chapter three.

26.   **C. Parent's relationship to exercise.** For more information, see "Social Support" in chapter three.

27.   **D. When someone engages in the behavior with someone else.** For more information, see "Social Support" in chapter three.

28.   **B. Accountability and comradery.** For more information, see "Social Support" in chapter three.

29.   **A. Planning and self-monitoring.** For more information, see "Behavioral Coaching" in chapter three.

30.   **A. When a person believes that a stimulus is pleasant or enjoyable.** For more information on positive affective judgments, see "Designing a Program" in chapter three.

31.   **A. More likely to do so.** For more information on subjective norms, see "Designing a Program" in chapter three.

32.   **D. Progress to the point of readiness.** For more information, see the last paragraph of "Designing a Program" in chapter three.

33.   **D. Precontemplation stage.** For more information, see the last paragraph in the "Designing a Program" section of chapter three.

34.   **C. Asking questions, reflecting, summarizing, affirming, and asking permission.** For more information, see "Communication with the Client" in chapter three.

35.   **B. It leaves no room for ambiguity, answers questions clearly.** For more information, see "Developing a Behavioral Change Technique" in chapter three.

36. **B. Will help a client begin to exercise and follow through with goals.** For more information, see "Developing a Behavioral Change Technique (BCT)."

37. **B. Medical conditions that prohibit the client from exercise.** For more information, see the introduction to chapter four.

38. **B. Ways to noninvasively measure nutritional status and amounts of body fat.** For more information, see "Anthropometry" in chapter four.

39. **D. Hydrostatic underwater weighing.** For more information, see "Hydrostatic Underwater Weighing" in chapter four.

40. **A. The waist, neck, chest, hips, thighs, calves, and arms.** For more information, see "Anthropometry" in chapter four.

41. **B. Information about progression over time.** For more information, see "Anthropometry" in chapter four.

42. **B. Healthy.** For more information, see "Anthropometry" in chapter four.

43. **C. Breathing is audible and the client is having difficulty catching their breath.** For more information, see "The Ventilatory Threshold (VT) Test" section of chapter four.

44. **A. Glucose.** For more information, see "The Ventilatory Threshold (VT) Test" section of chapter four.

45. **C. Joints.** For more information, see "Static Posture" in chapter four.

46. **C. Upper crossed syndrome.** For more information, see "Static Posture" in chapter four.

47. **A. Feet, ankles, knees, lumbo-pelvic-hip complex, shoulders, head, and neck.** For more information, see "Dynamic Posture" in chapter four.

48. **C. Feet or knees changing position, back arching, arms falling forward, or difficulty keeping balance.** For more information, see "Dynamic Posture" in chapter four.

49. **B. Find a one-rep max.** For more information, see "Push-up and Jump Tests" in chapter four.

50. **A. Yes, reassessment demonstrates progress and improvement.** For more information, see the introduction to chapter four.

51. **D. It can identify health concerns.** For more information, see "Blood Pressure" in chapter four.

52. **B. No, this is within the healthy blood pressure range.** For more information, see "Blood Pressure" in chapter four.

53. **A. Variations in weight, size, and proportion can impact health goals and monitor progress.** For more information, see "Anthropometry" in chapter four.

54. **C. A single-leg squat.** For more information, see "Dynamic Posture" in chapter four.

55. **A. It assigns a numerical value based on weight and height.** For more information, see "Anthropometry" in chapter four.

56. **B. It increases the likelihood of sticking to a fitness routine.** For more information, see the introduction to chapter five.

57. **C. The weekly outline.** For more information, see "Training Cycles" in chapter five.

58. **A. Adaptability and response.** For more information, see "The Optimum Performance Training (OPT) Model" in chapter five.

59. **B. Squat, hip hinge, pulling, pushing, pressing, and multiplanar movement.** For more information, see the "Level 1: Stabilization" subsection in chapter five.

60. **A. Stabilization.** For more information, see the "Level 1: Stabilization" subsection in chapter five.

61. **B. Strength.** For more information, see the "Level 2: Strength" subsection in chapter five.

62. **B. Activation.** For more information, see the "Level 3: Power" subsection in chapter five.

63. **D. Ease of use and less intimidation.** For more information, see "Strength Training Machines" in chapter five.

64. **C. Higher risk of injury.** For more information, see "Free Weights" in chapter five.

65. **A. Align the resistance angle with the line of pull.** For more information, see "Cable Machines" in chapter five.

66. **B. Elastic training.** For more information, see "Elastic Training" in chapter five.

67. **C. Battle ropes.** For more information, see "Battle Ropes" in chapter five.

68. **B. Increased core muscle activation, low spinal compression, increased balance, and better joint mobility.** For more information, see "Suspended Bodyweight Exercises" in chapter five.

69. **A. Large, round balls that increase the demand for stability and help with posture.** For more information, see "Proprioceptive Modalities" in chapter five.

70. **C. Useful for monitoring, accountability, and medical reasons.** For more information about fitness trackers, see "Keeping Track of Fitness."

71.   **B. Been on a steady decline.** For more information about children and adolescents, see "Chronic Health Conditions and Special Populations" in chapter five.

72.   **C. It is likely that more teens will become active adults.** For more information, see "Chronic Health Conditions and Special Populations" in chapter five.

73.   **A. Establish postural support before attempting free-standing exercise.** For more information, see "Health Conditions and Special Populations" in chapter five.

74.   **A. Type 2 diabetes.** For more information, see "Health Conditions and Special Populations" in chapter five.

75.   **D. Rheumatoid arthritis is when the body's immune system attacks joints, osteoarthritis is caused by mechanical wear and tear on the joints.** For more information, see "Health Conditions and Special Populations" in chapter five.

76.   **B. Coronary heart disease.** For more information, see "Health Conditions and Special Populations" in chapter five.

77.   **B. 1-2 repetitions at 40-70% intensity.** For more information, see "Health Conditions and Special Populations" in chapter five.

78.   **A. Delayed.** For more information, see "Health Conditions and Special Populations" in chapter five.

79.   **C. Stiffness, intense pain, and swelling in the joints.** For more information, see "Health Conditions and Special Populations" in chapter five.

80.   **C. Self-doubt and the higher possibility of injury.** For more information, see " Integrated Training and the OPT Model" in chapter six.

81.   **A. Helps the body become adapted to new demands.** For more information, see " Integrated Training and the OPT Model" in chapter six.

82.   **B. Yes, it will help the client understand the proper form.** For more information, see " Integrated Training and the OPT Model" in chapter six.

83.   **C. Muscular development training.** For more information, see "Goals of the 5 Phases of the OPT Model" in chapter six.

84.   **D. Increased force production.** For more information, see "Goals of the 5 Phases of the OPT Model" in chapter six.

85.   **A. Increase range of motion and extensibility of tissues.** For more information, see "Flexibility Training Concepts" in chapter six.

86.   **D. Upper and lower chains.** For more information, see " Flexibility Training Concepts" in chapter six.

87.   **C. The ability of the nervous system to utilize the correct muscles to complete a task.** For more information, see " Flexibility Training Concepts" in chapter six.

88.   **A. Repeatedly performing the same exercise or movement.** For more information, see "Pattern Overload and Cumulative Injury Cycle" in chapter six.

89.   **B. Cumulative injury cycle.** For more information, see "Pattern Overload and Cumulative Injury Cycle" in chapter six.

90.   **A. Static stretching takes the muscle through a passive point of tension and holds the stretch, active stretching uses both agonist and synergist muscles to move a joint through the full range of movement.** For more information, see "Types of Flexibility Training" in chapter six.

91.   **B. Cardiorespiratory fitness training.** For more information, see "Cardiorespiratory Fitness Training" in chapter six.

92.   **D. Volume.** For more information, see "Cardiorespiratory Fitness Training" in chapter six.

93. **A. To introduce individuals to higher intensity through interval training.** For more information, see "Cardiorespiratory Fitness Training" in chapter six.

94. **B. Give stability to the spine.** For more information, see "Core Training Concepts" in chapter six.

95. **B. Intervertebral stability helps with the stabilization of individual spinal segments, lumbopelvic stability helps with the stabilization of the lumbo-pelvic-hip complex.** For more information, see the "Designing a Core Training Program" subsection in chapter six.

96. **C. After both intervertebral and lumbopelvic stability.** For more information, see the "Designing a Core Training Program" subsection in chapter six.

97. **A. Lower extremity muscles.** For more information, see "Balance Training Concepts" in chapter six.

98. **D. Falls.** For more information, see "Balance Training Concepts" in chapter six.

99. **B. Vision, vestibular sense, and somatosensation.** For more information, see "Balance Training Concepts" in chapter six.

100. **A. Used to increase explosive movement.** For more information, see "Plyometric (Reactive) Training Concepts" in chapter six.

101. **C. The body's ability to decelerate, stabilize, and accelerate in a performance-based task.** For more information, see "Plyometric (Reactive) Training Concepts" in chapter six.

102. **A. Stabilization.** For more information, see "Plyometric (Reactive) Training Concepts" in chapter six.

103. **C. Increased performance and ability to recruit muscle fibers and distribute blood and oxygen.** For more information, see "Resistance Training Concepts" in chapter six.

104. **B. The speed of contraction and the selection of exercise.** For more information, see "The Specific Adaptations to Imposed Demands (SAID) Principle" in chapter six.

105. **D. Elements that can be manipulated to find the correct amount of stress to put on the body.** For more information, see "The Specific Adaptations to Imposed Demands (SAID) Principle" in chapter six.

106. **B. Split training.** For more information, see "The Specific Adaptations to Imposed Demands (SAID) Principle" in chapter six.

107. **A. Distance covered divided by the time it is covered.** For more information, see "Speed, Agility, and Quickness (SAQ) Training Concepts" in chapter six.

108. **C. Improved technical skills in the change of direction and sprinting mechanics.** For more information, see "Flexibility Training Concepts" in chapter six.

109. **C. It allows the client to move logically and safely from one stage to the next.** For more information, see "The Modern State of Health and Fitness" in chapter seven.

110. **B. These practices ensure that the client is receiving the best possible experience and the best possible results.** For more information, see "The Modern State of Health and Fitness" in chapter seven.

111. **D. A disease is a disorder that negatively affects the structure or function of the body.** For more information, see "Common concerns in modern health" in chapter seven.

112. **B. Overweight is less severe, obese is more severe, and poses the risk of more serious health risks.** For more information, see "Overweight and obese issues" in chapter seven.

113. **B. Type 1 and Type 2.** For more information, see "Diabetes" in chapter seven.

114. **D. Exercise can increase insulin sensitivity.** For more information, see "Diabetes" in chapter seven.

115. **A. A blood pressure greater than 120/80.** For more information, see "Heart issues" in chapter seven.

116. **B. Arteries to dilate more easily.** For more information, see "Heart issues" in chapter seven.

117. **C. Exercise can contribute to preventing some forms of cancer and can improve quality of life during treatment.** For more information, see "Cancer" in chapter seven.

118. **C. Ankle sprains and plantar fasciitis.** For more information, see "Muscular Dysfunction" in chapter seven.

119. **B. Respiratory.** For more information, see "Chronic Obstructive Pulmonary Disease (COPD)" in chapter seven.

120. **C. To address clients' health concerns.** For more information, see "Healthcare" in chapter seven.

Chapter Ten: Practice Test 3

1.   Which of the following is the correct definition of an organ system?

A. An organ that is part of one or more systems.
B. A collection of organs working together to accomplish the purpose of the system.
C. The collection of organs that make up the human body.
D. Complementary organs that fulfill a task.

2.   How many organ systems are in the human body?

A. Seven
B. Eleven
C. Fourteen
D. Twenty-three

3.   How many organ systems can be in poor working order if a person is considered healthy?

A. One organ system, as other systems will step in to compensate.
B. Up to three organ systems, more than this can result in organ failure.
C. All organ systems are essential to maintaining good health.
D. Organ systems are not essential to maintaining good health.

4.   Which of the following is the correct definition of neurons?

A. Cells that send electrical signals throughout the body.

B. Cells that control voluntary muscle movement.

C. Cells that control involuntary muscle movement.

D. Cells that make up the brain and spinal cord.

5. What is the difference between afferent and efferent?

  A. Afferent controls voluntary movement, efferent controls involuntary movement.

  B. Afferent controls involuntary movement, efferent controls voluntary movement.

  C. Afferent carries electrical impulses from the brain, efferent brings information to the brain.

  D. Afferent brings information to the brain, efferent carries electrical impulses from the brain.

6. To function and develop, the nervous system needs which of the following electrolytes?

  A. Phosphorus, calcium, and phosphate.

  B. Chloride, bicarbonate, boric acid, and glycine.

  C. Zinc, iron, and fluoride

  D. Sodium, potassium, magnesium, and water.

7. Which of the following is responsible for connecting bone to muscle?

  E. Tendons

  A. Intervertebral discs

  B. Joints

  C. Axial bones

8. The tibia bone is an example of:

  A. Long bones

  B. Short bones

  C. Flat bones

  D. Irregular bones

9. Which of the following regions of the spinal column is most important in providing stability during movement?

    A. The sacral region
    B. The lumbar region
    C. The thoracic region
    D. The cervical region

10. Which of the following is **not** a purpose of intervertebral discs?

    A. Shock absorption
    B. Flexible movement
    C. Stabilization
    D. Space between vertebrae

11. To shorten the muscle fiber, myosin filaments pull at which of the following filaments?

    A. Type One
    B. Type Two
    C. Polyamides
    D. Actin

12. What is the responsibility of the aortic and pulmonary valves?

    A. To move blood from upper chambers of the heart to lower chambers of the heart.
    B. To send blood through the pulmonary circuit.
    C. To move blood to the body.
    D. To contract the heart.

13. What is the responsibility of platelets?

    A. To carry oxygen
    B. To stop bleeding
    C. To detect infections
    D. To fight off infections

14.   What is the usual range of respiratory rate during rest?

A. 9-12 breaths per minute
B. 12-20 breaths per minute
C. 20-30 breaths per minute
D. 30-45 breaths per minute

15.   What is the difference between exocrine and endocrine glands?

A. Exocrine glands have ducts leading to the surface, and endocrine glands are ductless.
B. Exocrine glands are ductless, endocrine glands have ducts leading to the surface.
C. Exocrine glands are responsible for growth and development hormones, endocrine glands are responsible for metabolic hormones.
D. Exocrine glands are responsible for metabolic hormones, endocrine glands are responsible for growth and development hormones.

16.   Which of the following means "from the side?"

A. Medial
B. Contralateral
C. Ipsilateral
D. Lateral

17.   Which of the following will cause the muscle to have a limited ability to produce force?

A. Placing the muscle in an overly shortened or lengthened position.
B. Stretching a muscle before exercise.
C. Creating muscle tension without a change in muscle length.
D. Causing the muscle to lengthen when producing force.

18.   What is a force couple?

A. When one muscle performs a movement and the other keeps the origin of that muscle steady.

B. When an agonist needs an antagonist in order to contract.

C. When multiple forces act in different directions to cause a rotational motion.

D. When the local muscular system stabilizes joints during global movement.

19. A person's perception of the correct way to exercise is informed by:

A. Information and images from the media.
B. The example of family and friends.
C. Evidence-based practices.
D. A variety of factors.

20. Which of the following is not an accurate indicator of health?

A. Physical appearance
B. Blood pressure
C. Heart rate
D. Cholesterol levels

21. To encourage a client to share the aspects of exercise that are most important to them, which of the following is most essential?

A. Demonstrating that media images are unrealistic.
B. Communicating clearly about expectations.
C. Creating a list or vision board of fitness inspiration.
D. Sharing your personal values and goals.

22. Long-lasting behavior change comes through:

A. High-intensity behaviors.
B. Directing behaviors in a positive direction.
C. Development of new habits.
D. Waiting until obstacles are removed.

23. Which of the following is true about social support?

    A. Clients should use only pre-existing support.
    B. Physical trainers can recommend sources of social support.
    C. The physical trainer is the most important source of emotional support.
    D. Companionship support should come only from other clients.

24. When a physical trainer comes to work looking sloppy and in clothes that are not appropriate for the task at hand, which attribute are they failing to demonstrate?

    A. Professionalism
    B. Relationship-building
    C. Competency
    D. Accountability

25. When is self-monitoring applicable for clients?

    A. Self-monitoring applies to clients working with a physical trainer virtually, as their exercise is done on their own.
    B. Self-monitoring applies to clients who are in the maintenance stage, as they have proven that they can take action on their own.
    C. Self-monitoring applies to all clients, as it helps build self-efficacy.
    D. Self-monitoring does not apply to clients, as this is within the role of the physical trainer.

26. When a client does not exercise and does not plan to begin exercise within the next six months, which stage of the transtheoretical model of behavior change are they in?

    A. They are not yet in a stage of this model.
    B. They are in the precontemplation stage.
    C. They are in the contemplation stage.
    D. They are in the preparation stage.

ML

27.   When a client is exercising sporadically, which stage of the transtheoretical model of behavior change are they in?

   A. Contemplation stage
   B. Preparation stage
   C. Action stage
   D. Maintenance stage

28.   What is the purpose of the transtheoretical model of behavior change?

   A. Allows the trainer to assess the strength of a client's motivation.
   B. Prepares the client to move into the next stage more quickly.
   C. Allows the trainer to understand the client's views of exercise.
   D. Helps the trainer be able to best meet the needs of the client.

29.   What is the difference between verbal and non-verbal communication?

   A. Verbal communication relies on words and how words are said, nonverbal communication relies on facial expression, posture, and eye contact.
   B. Verbal communication relies on facial expression, posture, and eye contact, nonverbal communication relies on words and how words are said.
   C. Verbal communication asks the conversation partner for a response, nonverbal communication asks the conversation partner for an action.
   D. Verbal communication asks the conversation partner for an action, nonverbal communication asks the conversation partner for a response.

30.   When should a physical trainer observe the discrepancy between the client's current and ideal state?

   A. During motivational interviewing.
   B. When designing a program.
   C. When setting a SMART goal.
   D. Never.

31.   What is the purpose of motivational interviewing?

   A. Enhance internal motivation.

     B. Enhance external motivation.

     C. Create internal motivation.

     D. Create external motivation.

32. What is a behavioral change technique?

     A. Any form of enhancing motivation.

     B. When a trainer changes their behavior to connect to a client.

     C. A strategy that will help the client change.

     D. Moving from one stage of readiness to the next.

33. Which of the following is an example of a SMART goal for someone with an overarching strength goal?

     A. I will be able to perform my maximum deadlift with the correct form.

     B. By the end of the month, I will be able to perform my maximum deadlift with a straight back.

     C. In two weeks, I will be able to perform my mile time faster than I currently am.

     D. By the end of this training session, I will be able to increase my maximum deadlift by twenty pounds.

34. How can this goal be changed to become a SMART goal: I want to run faster.

     A. By the end of the week, I will run faster in the 400m dash.

     B. I will decrease my sprint time by five seconds in the 400m dash.

     C. By the end of the week, I will decrease my sprint time by five seconds.

     D. By the end of the month, I will decrease my 400m dash time by five seconds.

35. Which of the following is the correct definition of "relevant" as it relates to SMART goals?

     A. It leaves no room for ambiguity.

     B. It has a clear, monitored goal.

     C. It is in alignment with long-term goals.

     D. It helps the client consider ability and time.

36.   Which of the following is **not** something that a program design should be based upon?

    A. Client's abilities
    B. Client's health concerns
    C. Client's goals
    D. Client's support groups

37.   The order of the fitness assessments should move from:

    A. Highest comfort to least comfort in the activity.
    B. Least vigorous to most vigorous test.
    C. Internal to external measurements.
    D. General information to specific information.

38.   What happens to the heart rate as the heart and lungs grow more conditioned?

    A. Heart rate becomes more regular.
    B. Heart rate is easier to measure.
    C. Higher heart rate at rest.
    D. Lower heart rate at rest.

39.   If a client has a BMI of 18.2, what category are they in according to the Body Mass Index?

    A. Underweight
    B. Healthy
    C. Overweight
    D. Obese

40.   Which of the following is a drawback of circumference measurement?

    A. Variability in reading measurements.
    B. It does not provide baseline information.
    C. Does not demonstrate progress to clients.
    D. Takes time to learn proper measurement techniques.

41.   How does bioelectrical impedance work?

    A. Passes electricity through water to analyze the density of the body.
    B. Measures the level of electrical impulses it takes to contract muscles.
    C. Passes electricity through the body to analyze the amount of fat and muscle.
    D. Uses an X-ray to view the likely amounts of fat and muscle surrounding bone.

42.   VO2 Max tests measure the difference between which two elements?

    A. Heart rate and respiration rate.
    B. Inhaled and exhaled oxygen.
    C. Stroke volume and blood oxygen levels.
    D. Intensity and duration.

43.   When is static posture assessed?

    A. When the body is in movement.
    B. When the body is stretching.
    C. When the body is performing an exercise.
    D. When the body is standing.

44.   What is the difference between lower crossed syndrome and upper crossed syndrome?

    A. Lower crossed syndrome includes an anterior pelvic tilt and extension of the lumbar spine, and upper crossed syndrome includes a forward head and rounded shoulders.
    B. Lower crossed syndrome includes a forward head and rounded shoulders, and upper crossed syndrome includes an anterior pelvic tilt and extension of the lumbar spine.
    C. Lower crossed syndrome includes adducted and internally rotated hips, and upper crossed syndrome includes adducted and internally rotated shoulders.
    D. Lower crossed syndrome includes adducted and internally rotated shoulders, and upper crossed syndrome includes adducted and internally rotated hips.

45.   Which of the following does an overhead squat assessment **not** include?

A. Dynamic posture
B. Core stability
C. Lower body strength
D. Neuromuscular control

46.   Which assessment allows a physical trainer to monitor progress on a strength goal?

A. Push-up assessment
B. Benchpress weight assessment
C. Overhead squat assessment
D. Single-leg squat assessment

47.   Which of the following are physical assessments used for?

A. Tailor the exercise program to the client
B. Monitor the client's progress
C. Neither A or B
D. Both A and B

48.   Which of the following is true when implementing movement and performance exercises?

A. A physical trainer should continue to exercise caution throughout the process.
B. A physical trainer does not need to exercise caution once health assessments are complete.
C. A physical trainer should exercise caution for beginner-level movement assessments, but not for advanced performance assessments.
D. A physical trainer should exercise caution when introducing performance assessments, but not for movement assessments.

49.   Lower Extremity Functional Tests are used for what type of clients?

A. Those with weight loss or weight management goals.

B. Those who struggle with postural control.

C. Those with speed and performance goals.

D. Those with injuries to the lower extremities.

50. What is the purpose of a push-up test?

A. To measure muscular endurance in the upper body.

B. To find a one-rep max with added weight.

C. To check postural support in wrists and arms.

D. To build up to performance assessments.

51. Which exercise is the basis for all other movement assessments?

A. Push-up and pull-up tests

B. VO2 Max tests

C. Talk tests, including VT1 and VT2

D. Overhead squat

52. Which of the following is not assessed during a single-leg squat assessment?

A. Strength

B. Endurance

C. Balance

D. Coordination

53. Which of the following decreases stress on the joints?

A. Movement

B. Performance

C. Posture

D. Strength

54. Which of the following is a true statement about anthropometry?

A. Anthropometry is the study of human beings.

B. There is one best practice to assess variations in weight, size, and proportion.

C. Anthropometric measurements are invasive.

D. Anthropometric measurements compare health by measuring nutritional status and amount of body fat.

55.   What variances in weight does the Body Mass Index take into account?

A. Lean muscle
B. Genetic predisposition
C. Pregnancy
D. None of the above

56.   Which of the following is the correct definition of periodization?

A. An approach to designing programs that splits the plan into distinct cycles.

B. An approach to designing programs that dictates the time spent.

C. An approach to designing programs that customize the plan to the needs of the client.

D. An approach to designing programs that best match the client's goals.

57.   Which of the following is a true statement about the Optimum Performance Training (OPT) model?

A. It will allow a client to improve in 1-2 aspects.
B. It has a total of eight levels.
C. It is a way to balance linear and nonlinear approaches.
D. It is a way to systematically plan a periodized program.

58.   Developing proper movement patterns and improving movement and stability throughout the kinetic chain is the goal of which level in the Optimum Performance Training Model?

A. Stabilization
B. Strength
C. Power

D. Endurance

59. The strength level of the Optimum Performance Model focuses on increasing the recruitment of more motor units to overcome an external load, which is also known as:

    A. Stretch-shortening
    B. Volume of training
    C. Maximal strength
    D. Increased metabolic demand

60. What mental and emotional skills are explicitly taught in the stabilization stage?

    A. Knowledge of program design and resilience.
    B. Knowledge of various machines and greater confidence.
    C. Knowledge of social support and motivation.
    D. Knowledge of habit change and better behaviors.

61. What is the best way to train for power?

    A. Heavy loads with high intensity at low repetitions.
    B. Heavy loads with low intensity at high repetitions.
    C. Heavy loads with high intensity at high repetitions.
    D. Heavy loads with low intensity at low repetitions.

62. Which of the following is **not** a part of the six-step daily workout?

    A. Client's choice of activity
    B. Skill development
    C. Resistance training
    D. Cardiorespiratory training

63. What is the main purpose of the many different training modalities?

    A. Different modalities appeal to different clients.
    B. Each modality is designed to encourage a different reaction.

C. Different modalities train different organ systems.

D. To vary the intensity of an exercise.

64.   What is a requirement for training for functionality?

A. Working in a combination of endurance and strength.

B. Training on an unstable surface.

C. Working in all planes of movement.

D. Training using performance-based exercise.

65.   Which of the following has the greatest risk for injury, especially for beginners?

A. Strength training machines

B. Free weights

C. Elastic training

D. Battle ropes

66.   Which of the following modalities offers a hybrid between the free movement of free weights and the security of strength training machines?

A. Battle ropes

B. Elastic training

C. Bodyweight exercises

D. Cable machines

67.   What is the main drawback of elastic training?

A. Adjustments to the line of pull

B. Loss of elasticity

C. Expense

D. Does not work muscles, only joints

68.   Which is the correct description of a kettlebell?

A. Flat-bottomed iron balls with handles on top.

B. A short bar with a weight at each end.

C. A rubber tube with handles and openings at both ends.

D. Hemispheres with half a ball attached to a hard plastic surface.

69. Why are kettlebells difficult to get used to?

    A. Handles require greater grip strength.
    B. Different movement patterns are required.
    C. They have a lower center of gravity.
    D. They provide functional training.

70. What is the best way to add resistance to bodyweight exercises?

    A. Variations on the exercise.
    B. Adding weight to the body.
    C. Increasing the intensity.
    D. Using circuit training.

71. What materials are needed for suspended body weight training?

    A. A cable machine and a weight that is approximately the same as bodyweight.
    B. Several elastics.
    C. Only the weight provided by the body.
    D. Rope or webbing.

72. Which of the following is **not** a benefit of suspended bodyweight training?

    A. High-impact muscular training.
    B. Increased core muscle activation.
    C. Increased joint mobility.
    D. Low spinal compression.

73. Which of the following is **not** a benefit of sandbag training?

    A. Mimics real-life functionality.
    B. High levels of precision.
    C. Shifting weight challenges stability and balance.
    D. Can be adjusted easily.

74. Which of the following is the focus of ViPR training?

    A. Full-body workout.
    B. Developing bone density.
    C. Load movement.
    D. Endurance training.

75. Which of the following proprioceptive modalities help with posture during squatting?

    A. Stability balls
    B. Bosu balls
    C. Terra-core
    D. Lower Extremity Functional Test

76. Which of the following should fitness trackers not be used for?

    A. Monitoring
    B. Accountability
    C. Medical reasons
    D. Gauging success

77. Why are children incapable of sustaining much high-intensity exercise?

    A. They do not produce enough glycolytic enzymes.
    B. They have limited type two muscle fibers.
    C. They quickly become bored with exertion.
    D. Their hearts do not pump blood more quickly based on higher oxygen needs.

78. Which system is delayed in children?

    A. Cardiorespiratory
    B. Thermoregulatory
    C. Endocrine
    D. Digestive

79. Which statement is true about exercise?

    A. Exercise does not control the amount of glucose in the body, but does allow the body to use energy during exercise.
    B. Exercise controls the amount of glucose in the body, but does not allow the body to use energy during activity.
    C. Exercise controls the amount of glucose in the body, and allows the body to use energy during activity.
    D. Exercise does not control the amount of glucose in the body and does not allow the body to use energy during exercise.

80. Increasing the muscle force-generating capacity is a goal of which phase in the Optimum Performance Training Model?

    A. Strength endurance training
    B. Muscular development training
    C. Maximal strength training
    D. Power training

81. Increasing the rate of production is a goal of which phase in the Optimum Performance Training Model?

    A. Strength endurance training
    B. Muscular development training
    C. Maximal strength training
    D. Power training

82. How does poor flexibility impact movement patterns?

    A. The body will attempt to complete the movement with the least amount of resistance, leading to poor form, injury, or incomplete movement.
    B. The body will become more adaptable, improving joint strength and resilience, and leading to injury prevention.
    C. The body will naturally adjust to a limited range of motion, meaning that movement patterns will only be trivially affected.
    D. The body will improve in other areas, including muscular strength

and coordination, which will ultimately assist in completing movement patterns.

83. Which is the correct definition of the kinetic chain?

    A. Joints that are essential to stability and movement
    B. The human movement system
    C. Fundamental connections throughout the human body
    D. Key points that must be in alignment for proper movement

84. Which of the following can a lack of neuromuscular efficiency lead to?

    A. Muscle imbalances
    B. Slowed muscle contractions
    C. Ineffective stretch-shortening cycle
    D. Altered joint motion

85. Practicing a movement incorrectly will cause which of the following?

    A. Eventual balance as the body corrects itself
    B. Continued incorrect performance
    C. A cumulative injury cycle
    D. Better preparation for correct movement

86. A client struggles to consistently move through a full range of movements. Which type of stretching will help them practice that skill?

    A. Self-myofascial techniques
    B. Static stretching
    C. Active stretching
    D. Squatting

87. For cardiorespiratory training, an individual decides to work in a state in which they are breathing hard, with a higher-than-normal pulse and respiration rate, but without breathlessness or exhaustion. This falls under which components of cardiorespiratory training?

    A. Frequency
    B. Intensity
    C. Progression
    D. Type

88. A client and physical trainer are working together to decide on the number of training periods within a set time. This falls under which component of cardiorespiratory training?

    A. Frequency
    B. Intensity
    C. Progression
    D. Type

89. Low-intensity yoga would likely fall into which of the four cardiorespiratory training zones?

    A. Zone One
    B. Zone Two
    C. Zone Three
    D. Zone Four

90. Which stage of the cardiorespiratory exercise training session is meant for athletes, focusing on linear, multidirectional, and sport-specific activities?

    A. Stage Two
    B. Stage Three
    C. Stage Four
    D. Stage Five

91.   Which of the following is true about local muscles?

A. They attach to or near vertebrae and are mainly type one muscle fibers.
B. They attach directly to vertebrae, not just near, and are mainly type one muscle fibers.
C. They attach to or near vertebrae and are mainly type two muscle fibers.
D. They attach directly to vertebrae, not just near, and are mainly type two muscle fibers.

92.   Which is the desired outcome of movement efficiency?

A. Decreased neuromuscular delay.
B. Improved movement quality and force output.
C. Increased oxygen utilization and decreased heart rate.
D. Greater accuracy and speed.

93.   Which of these exercises are **not** beneficial for movement efficiency?

A. Rotation chest passes
B. Overhead crunch throws
C. Soccer throws
D. One-arm hang

94.   Which of the following is the correct term for outward curves of the thoracic and sacral spine?

A. Lordotic curves
B. Kyphotic curves
C. Scoliosis
D. Osteoporosis

95.   Which of the following is caused by abnormal curvatures of the spine?

A. Incorrect movement patterns
B. Inability to create acetin
C. A combination of overactive and underactive muscles
D. Inability to complete basic core training movements without variations

96. Which of the following is **not** improved by balance training?

    A. Landing mechanics
    B. Proprioception
    C. Lower body muscular strength
    D. Upper body muscular strength

97. Which of the following is included in somatosensation:

    A. Pressure
    B. Vision
    C. Color differentiation
    D. Posture

98. Which form of balance allows the center of gravity to continuously change?

    A. Static
    B. Semi-dynamic
    C. Dynamic
    D. Explosive

99. Which of the key checkpoints should be monitored during balance exercises?

    A. Feet, ankles, and knees.
    B. Feet, ankles, knees, and lumbo-pelvic-hip complex.
    C. Feet, ankles, knees, lumbo-pelvic-hip complex, and shoulders.
    D. Feet, ankles, knees, lumbo-pelvic-hip complex, shoulders, and head/cervical spine.

100. Which of the following is **not** a benefit of plyometric training?

    A. Increased bone density.
    B. Soft tissue strength.
    C. Improved semi-static balance.
    D. Improved weight management.

101. Which of the following is **not** part of the integrated performance paradigm?

A. Stabilization
B. Amortization
C. Deceleration
D. Acceleration

102. Which is the correct order of the stretch-shortening cycle?

A. Eccentric, amortization, and concentric phases.
B. Amortization, concentric, and eccentric phases.
C. Concentric, eccentric, and amortization phases.
D. Eccentric, concentric, and amortization phases.

103. At what tempo should exercises be completed in the power phase of plyometric exercise?

A. Easy tempo
B. Steady tempo
C. Mid-tempo
D. As quickly as possible

104. Which of the following can result from an alarm reaction in the General Adaptation Syndrome?

A. Stress fractures
B. Joint pain
C. Delayed onset muscle soreness
D. Muscle exhaustion

105. What is metabolic specificity?

A. The energy demands placed on the body
B. The speed of muscle contraction
C. The weight and movement put on the body
D. The caloric needs of an individual before exercise

106.   Muscle fibers are enlarged in response to which of the following?

    A. Adequate joint support
    B. Developing tension levels
    C. Force production
    D. Time spent maintaining force

107.   Which of the following is the best definition of strength?

    A. The ability to produce and maintain force production for a long time.
    B. Enlargement of muscle fibers and development of muscles.
    C. The ability to make the most force possible in the shortest amount of time.
    D. The ability of the neuromuscular system to produce tension internally.

108.   Which of the following is the correct term for using 1-2 sets at lower intensities to prepare the body for more intense exercise?

    A. Warm-up set
    B. Single set
    C. Drop sets
    D. Peripheral heart action

109.   What does it mean to use evidence-based practice?

    A. To ask the client about exercise programs that have been most effective for them in the past.
    B. To share client information to collaborate with other professionals about what works most effectively
    C. To conscientiously use the current best evidence when making decisions about client care.
    D. To build the best possible relationship between the athlete and trainer, so the client feels confident about receiving good results.

110.   Which of the following is not a cardiovascular disease?

    A. Asthma
    B. Strokes

C. Heart failure

D. Arrhythmia

111.   What is a healthy level of LDLs?

A. Lower than 100 mg per deciliter

B. From 100-120 mg per deciliter

C. From 120-180 mg per deciliter

D. Above 180 mg per deciliter

112.   Which type of diabetes creates insulin resistance?

A. Type One

B. Type Two

C. Type Three

D. Type Four

113.   How many types of cancer are there?

A. Three.

B. Anywhere from 30-50.

C. Almost 100.

D. Hundreds.

114.   What types of cancer can be put in remission by exercise?

A. Leukemias

B. Lymphomas and myeloma

C. Carcinomas and sarcomas

D. Cancer cannot be put into remission by exercise

115.   Which of the following is **not** a characteristic of chronic obstructive pulmonary disease (COPD)?

A. Breathlessness

B. Lightheadedness

C. Limitations in airflow

D. Accelerated decline in lung function

116. What is the correct definition of plantar fasciitis?

   A. Stretching or tearing of ligaments in the ankle.
   B. Fractures in tarsal bones.
   C. Impingement of tissue and bone in the ankle.
   D. Tissue inflammation in the bottom of the foot.

117. What is the best way to describe the relationship between a physical trainer and their allied health professionals?

   A. A bridge between clients and licensed healthcare providers.
   B. An overseer to their allied health professionals.
   C. A fellow healthcare provider.
   D. Someone who can step into the role of a health professional when necessary.

118. What resource will answer further questions about the scope of practice as a physical trainer, and can ensure that the client and profession are protected?

   A. Fellow physical trainers
   B. Signage posted in gyms
   C. Allied healthcare professionals
   D. NASM Code of Professional Conduct

119. Which personal training practice option allows the physical trainer to set their own pay rates, but requires them to pay operational costs?

   A. Commercial health clubs
   B. Independent professional
   C. Small-group training
   D. Large-group training

120. Which personal training practice option is the most common for physical trainers?

A. Commercial health clubs
B. Independent professional
C. Small-group training
D. Online fitness coaching

Answer Key

Q.	1	2	3	4	5	6	7	8	9	10	11	12
A.	B	B	C	A	D	D	A	A	B	C	D	C

Q.	13	14	15	16	17	18	19	20	21	22	23	24
A.	B	B	A	D	A	C	D	A	B	C	B	A

Q.	25	26	27	28	29	30	31	32	33	34	35	36
A.	C	B	D	A	A	A	C	B	D	C	B	D

Q.	37	38	39	40	41	42	43	44	45	46	47	48
A.	B	D	A	B	C	B	D	A	C	B	D	A

Q.	49	50	51	52	53	54	55	56	57	58	59	60
A.	C	A	D	B	C	D	D	A	D	A	C	B

Q.	61	62	63	64	65	66	67	68	69	70	71	72
A.	A	D	B	C	B	D	B	A	C	B	D	A

Q.	73	74	75	76	77	78	79	80	81	82	83	84
A.	B	C	A	D	A	B	C	C	D	A	B	A

Q.	85	86	87	88	89	90	91	92	93	94	95	96
A.	B	C	B	A	A	D	A	B	D	B	C	D

Q.	97	98	99	100	101	102	103	104	105	106	107	108
A.	A	C	D	C	B	A	D	C	A	B	D	A

Q.	109	110	111	112	113	114	115	116	117	118	119	120
A.	C	A	A	B	C	D	B	D	A	D	B	A

Answer Explanations

1.   **B. A collection of organs working together to accomplish the purpose of the system.** For more information, see the introduction to chapter two.

2.   **B. Eleven.** For more information, see the introduction to chapter two.

3.   **C. All organ systems are essential to maintaining good health.** For more information, see the introduction to chapter two.

4.   **A. Cells that send electrical signals throughout the body.** For more information, see "The Nervous System" in chapter two.

5.   **D. Afferent brings information to the brain, efferent carries electrical impulses from the brain.** For more information, see the "Sensory and Motor Systems" subsection in chapter two.

6.   **D. Sodium, potassium, magnesium, and water.** For more information, see "The Structure of the Nervous System" subsection in chapter two.

7.   **A. Tendons.** For more information, see "The Skeletal System" in chapter two.

8.   **A. Long bones.** For more information, see "The Skeletal System" in chapter two.

9.   **B. The lumbar region.** For more information, see "The Vertebral Column" in chapter two.

10. **C. Stabilization.** For more information, see "The Vertebral Column" in chapter two.

11. **D. Actin.** For more information, see the "How Muscles Work" subsection in chapter two.

12. **C. To move blood to the body.** For more information, see "The Cardiorespiratory System" in chapter two.

13.   **B. To stop bleeding.** For more information, see "The Cardiorespiratory System" in chapter two.

14.   **B. 12-20 breaths per minute.** For more information, see the "Diffusion of Gasses" subsection in chapter two.

15.   **A. Exocrine glands have ducts leading to the surface, endocrine glands are ductless.** For more information, see "The Endocrine System" in chapter two.

16.   **D. Lateral.** For more information, see "Human Movement Science" in chapter two.

17.   **A. Placing the muscle in an overly shortened or lengthened position.** For more information, see "Human Movement Science" in chapter two.

18.   **C. When multiple forces act in different directions to cause a rotational motion.** For more information, see "Human Movement Science" in chapter two.

19.   **D. A variety of factors.** For more information, see the introduction to chapter three.

20.   **A. Physical appearance.** For more information, see the introduction to chapter three.

21.   **B. Communicating clearly about expectations.** For more information, see the introduction to chapter three.

22.   **C. Development of new habits.** For more information, see "The Psychology of Exercise" in chapter three.

23.   **B. Physical trainers can recommend sources of social support.** For more information, see "Social Support" in chapter three.

24.   **A. Professionalism.** For more information, see "Behavioral Coaching" in chapter three.

25. **C. Self-monitoring applies to all clients, as it helps build self-efficacy.** For more information, see "Designing a Program" in chapter three.

26. **B. They are in the precontemplation stage.** For more information, see "Designing a Program" in chapter three.

27. **D. Helps the trainer be able to best meet the needs of the client.** For more information, see "Designing a Program" in chapter three.

28. **A. Verbal communication relies on words and how words are said, nonverbal communication relies on facial expression, posture, and eye contact.** For more information, see "Communication with the Client" in chapter three.

29. **A. During motivational interviewing.** For more information, see "Communication with the Client" in chapter three.

30. **A. Enhance internal motivation.** For more information, see "Communication with the Client" in chapter three.

31. **C. A strategy that will help the client change.** For more information, see "Developing a Behavioral Change Technique (BCT)" in chapter three.

32. **B. By the end of the month, I will be able to perform my maximum deadlift with a straight back.** For more information, see "Developing a Behavioral Change Technique (BCT)" in chapter three.

33. **D. By the end of the month, I will decrease my 400m dash time by five seconds.** For more information, see "Developing a Behavioral Change Technique (BCT)" in chapter three.

34. **C. It is in alignment with long-term goals.** For more information, see "Developing a Behavioral Change Technique (BCT)" in chapter three.

35. **B. Preparation stage.** For more information, see "Designing a Program" in chapter three.

36.   **D. Client's support groups.** For more information, see "Designing a Program" in chapter three.

37.   **B. Least vigorous to most vigorous test.** For more information, see "Assessing Physical Fitness" in chapter four.

38.   **D. Lower heart rate at rest.** For more information, see "The Heart" in chapter four.

39.   **A. Underweight.** For more information, see "Anthropometry" in chapter four.

40.   **B. It does not provide baseline information.** For more information, see "Anthropometry" in chapter four.

41.   **C. Passes electricity through the body to analyze the amount of fat and muscle.** For more information, see "Bioelectrical Impedance Analysis" in chapter four.

42.   **B. Inhaled and exhaled oxygen.** For more information, see "The VO2 Max Test" in chapter four.

43.   **D. When the body is standing.** For more information, see "Static Posture" in chapter four.

44.   **A. Lower crossed syndrome includes an anterior pelvic tilt and extension of the lumbar spine, upper crossed syndrome includes a forward head and rounded shoulders.** For more information, see "Static Posture" in chapter four.

45.   **C. Lower body strength.** For more information, see "Dynamic Posture" in chapter four.

46.   **B. Bench press weight assessment.** For more information, see "Push-up and Jump Tests" in chapter four.

47. **D. Both A and B.** For more information, see "Performance Assessments" in chapter four.

48. **A. A physical trainer should continue to exercise caution throughout the process.** For more information, see "Performance Assessments" in chapter four.

49. **C. Those with speed and performance goals.** For more information, see "The Lower Extremity Functional Test" in chapter four.

50. **A. To measure muscular endurance in the upper body.** For more information, see "Push-up and Jump Tests" in chapter four.

51. **D. Overhead squat.** For more information, see "Dynamic Posture" in chapter four.

52. **B. Endurance.** For more information, see "Dynamic Posture" in chapter four.

53. **C. Posture.** For more information, see "Posture, Movement, and Performance Assessments" in chapter four.

54. **D. Anthropometric measurements compare health by measuring nutritional status and amount of body fat.** For more information, see "Anthropometry" in chapter four.

55. **D. None of the above.** For more information, see "Anthropometry" in chapter four.

56. **A. An approach to designing programs that splits the plan into distinct cycles.** For more information, see "The Optimum Performance Training (OPT) Model" in chapter five.

57. **D. It is a way to systematically plan a periodized program.** For more information, see "Linear Periodization" in chapter five.

58. **A. Stabilization.** For more information, see the "Level 1: Stabilization" subsection in chapter five.

59. **C. Maximal strength.** For more information, see the "Level 2: Strength" subsection in chapter five.

60. **B. Knowledge of various machines and greater confidence.** For more information, see the "Level 2: Strength" subsection in chapter five.

61. **A. Heavy loads with high intensity at low repetitions.** For more information, see the "Level 3: Power" subsection in chapter five.

62. **D. Cardiorespiratory training.** For more information, see the list below the "Level 3: Power" subsection in chapter five.

63. **B. Each modality is designed to encourage a different reaction.** For more information, see "Introduction to Exercise Modalities" in chapter five.

64. **C. Working in all planes of movement.** For more information, see "Strength Training Machines" in chapter five.

65. **B. Free weights.** For more information on the strengths and weaknesses of free weights, see "Free Weights" in chapter five.

66. **D. Cable machines.** For more information, see "Cable Machines" in chapter five.

67. **B. Loss of elasticity.** For more information, see "Elastic Training" in chapter five.

68. **A. Flat-bottomed iron balls with handles on top.** For more information, see "Kettlebell Training" in chapter five.

69. **C. They have a lower center of gravity.** For more information, see "Kettlebell Training" in chapter five.

70. **B. Adding weight to the body.** For more information, see "Bodyweight Exercises" in chapter five.

71. **D. Rope or webbing.** For more information, see "Suspended Bodyweight Training" in chapter five.

72.   **A. High-impact muscular training.** For more information, see "Suspended Bodyweight Training" in chapter five.

73.   **B. High levels of precision.** For more information, see "Sandbags" in chapter five.

74.   **C. Load movement.** For more information, see "ViPR" in chapter five.

75.   **A. Stability balls.** For more information, see "Proprioceptive Modalities" in chapter five.

76.   **D. Gauging success.** For more information, see "Keeping Track of Fitness" in chapter five.

77.   **A. They do not produce enough glycolytic enzymes.** For more information, see "Chronic Health Conditions and Special Populations" in chapter five.

78.   **B. Thermoregulatory.** For more information, see "Chronic Health Conditions and Special Populations" in chapter five.

79.   **C. Exercise controls the amount of glucose in the body and allows the body to use energy during activity.** For more information, see "Chronic Health Conditions and Special Populations" in chapter five.

80.   **C. Maximal strength training.** For more information about the five phases, see "Goals of the 5 Phases of the OPT Model" in chapter six.

81.   **D. Power training.** For more information about the five phases, see "Goals of the 5 Phases of the OPT Model" in chapter six.

82.   **A. The body will attempt to complete the movement with the least amount of resistance, leading to poor form, injury, or incomplete movement.** For more information, see "Flexibility Training Concepts" in chapter six.

83.   **B. The human movement system.** For more information, see "Flexibility Training Concepts" in chapter six.

84.   **A. Muscle imbalances.** For more information, see "Flexibility Training Concepts" in chapter six.

85.   **B. Continued incorrect performance.** For more information, see "Pattern Overload and Cumulative Injury Cycle" in chapter six.

86.   **C. Active stretching.** For more information, see "Types of Flexibility Training" in chapter six.

87.   **B. Intensity.** For more information, see "Cardiovascular Fitness Training" in chapter six.

88.   **A. Frequency.** For more information, see "Cardiovascular Fitness Training" in chapter six.

89.   **A. Zone one.** For more information, see "Cardiovascular Fitness Training" in chapter six.

90.   **D. Stage five.** For more information, see "Cardiovascular Fitness Training" in chapter six.

91.   **A. They attach on or near vertebrae, and are mainly type one muscle fibers.** For more information, see "Core Training Concepts" in chapter six.

92.   **B. Improved movement quality and force output.** For more information, see the "Designing a core training program" subsection in chapter six.

93.   **D. One-arm hang.** For more information, see the "Designing a core training program" subsection in chapter six.

94.   **B. Kyphotic curves.** For more information, see the "Abnormal Curvatures" subsection in chapter six.

95.   **C. A combination of overactive and underactive muscles.** For more information, see the "Abnormal curvatures" subsection in chapter six.

96. **D. Upper body muscular strength.** For more information, see "Balance Training Concepts" in chapter six.

97. **A. Pressure.** For more information, see "Balance Training Concepts" in chapter six.

98. **C. Dynamic.** For more information, see "Balance Training Concepts" in chapter six.

99. **D. Feet, ankles, knees, lumbo-pelvic-hip complex, shoulders, and head/cervical spine.** For more information, see "Balance Training Concepts" in chapter six.

100. **C. Improved semi-static balance.** For more information, see "Plyometric (Reactive) Training Concepts" in chapter six.

101. **B. Amortization.** For more information, see "Plyometric (Reactive) Training Concepts" in chapter six.

102. **A. Eccentric, amortization, and concentric phases.** For more information, see "Plyometric (Reactive) Training Concepts" in chapter six.

103. **D. As quickly as possible.** For more information, see "Plyometric (Reactive) Training Concepts" in chapter six.

104. **C. Delayed onset muscle soreness.** For more information, see "Resistance Training Concepts" in chapter six.

105. **A. The energy demands placed on the body.** For more information, see "The Specific Adaptations to Imposed Demands (SAID) Principle" in chapter six.

106. **B. Developing tension levels.** For more information, see "The Specific Adaptations to Imposed Demands (SAID) Principle" in chapter six.

107. **D. The ability of the neuromuscular system to produce tension internally.** For more information, see "The Specific Adaptations to Imposed Demands (SAID) Principle" in chapter six.

108.   **A. Warm-up set.** For more information, see "The Specific Adaptations to Imposed Demands (SAID) Principle" in chapter six.

109.   **C. To conscientiously use the current best evidence when making decisions about client care.** For more information, see "The Modern State of Health and Fitness" in chapter seven.

110.   **A. Asthma.** For more information, see "Heart Issues" in chapter seven.

111.   **A. Lower than 100 mg per deciliter.** For more information, see "Heart Issues" in chapter seven.

112.   **B. Type Two.** For more information, see "Diabetes" in chapter seven.

113.   **C. Almost 100.** For more information, see "Cancer" in chapter seven.

114.   **D. Cancer cannot be put into remission by exercise.** For more information, see "Cancer" in chapter seven.

115.   **B. Lightheadedness.** For more information, see "Chronic Obstructive Pulmonary Disease (COPD)" in chapter seven.

116.   **D. Tissue inflammation in the bottom of foot.** For more information, see "Muscular Dysfunction" in chapter seven.

117.   **A. A bridge between clients and licensed healthcare providers.** For more information, see "Healthcare" in chapter seven.

118.   **D. NASM Code of Professional Conduct.** For more information, see "Healthcare" in chapter seven.

119.   **B. Independent professional.** For more information, see "Personal Training Profession" in chapter seven.

120.   **A. Commercial health clubs.** For more information, see "Personal Training Profession" in chapter seven.

Final Words

With this wealth of information and practice tests to refer back to, you should now feel better prepared to succeed on the NASM CPT Exam. If you do not yet feel ready for the exam, remember the ACT principle, which will help you to be aware, combat, and excel as you prepare. You have all the tools you need for success in the exam and your career.

There are many things that you have learned in this book. You have learned the essential science behind the human body, from organ systems to movement science to basic nutrition. The psychology behind behavioral coaching and client relations has prepared you to succeed. You have learned assessment techniques and how to properly carry them out. With the Optimum Performance Training Model, you are now prepared to design programs in many different modalities and for many different populations.

You have also learned about various exercise techniques and training styles. And you have also learned more about the physical training profession and your place in it. If you feel that you have not yet mastered all these concepts, do not let test anxiety hold you back. There is still time to learn these topics. There is no reason to go into your exam feeling that you have not mastered these concepts.

Remember that many students have succeeded in this exam before. By putting forth the effort to review this material, you have already set yourself up for success in this exam. With this all-in-one study guide, you have everything you need to overcome obstacles to your success.

References

"8 Tips to Reduce Test Anxiety." *Coursera*, 15 June 2023, www.coursera.org/articles/test-anxiety-tips.

Baum, Howie. *The Muscular System*.

Capritto, Amanda. "Why Your Perception of Fit Is Probably Wrong (and the Reality of What's True)." *InBody USA*, 28 Nov. 2018, inbodyusa.com/blogs/inbodyblog/why-your-perception-of-fit-is-probably-wrong-and-the-reality-of-whats-true/.

"Causes of Test Anxiety." *Loma Linda University School of Medicine*, medicine.llu.edu/academics/resources/causes-test-anxiety.

Cherry, Kendra. "What Is Test Anxiety?" *Verywell Mind*, 30 May 2023, www.verywellmind.com/what-is-test-anxiety-2795368.

Cleveland Clinic. "Endocrine System." *Cleveland Clinic*, 5 Dec. 2020, my.clevelandclinic.org/health/body/21201-endocrine-system.

Cleveland Clinic. "Muscle." *Cleveland Clinic*, 29 Sept. 2021, my.clevelandclinic.org/health/body/21887-muscle.

Davidson, Katey. "A Guide to Body Planes and Their Movements." *Healthline*, 13 July 2022, www.healthline.com/health/body-planes.

"Fitness Instructor Demographics and Statistics in the US." *Zippia*, 29 Jan. 2021, www.zippia.com/fitness-instructor-jobs/demographics/.

Golden, Nicole. "The Benefits of Flexibility: Why You Should Stretch More!" *NASM*, blog.nasm.org/the-benefits-of-flexibility.

Golden, Nicole. "The Benefits of Flexibility: Why You Should Stretch More!" *NASM*, blog.nasm.org/the-benefits-of-flexibility.

"How to Overcome Test Anxiety." *Mometrix*, 25 Jan. 2017, www.mometrix.com/academy/test-anxiety-tips/.

"Human Skeletal System." *BYJUS*, byjus.com/biology/skeletal-system/.

Joubert, Shayna. "What Is Human Movement Science & Why Is It Important?" *Graduate Blog*, 5 Oct. 2021, graduate.northeastern.edu/resources/what-is-human-movement-science/.

Kitts, David. "Carbohydrate Digestion and Absorption." *Sugar*, sugar.ca/sugars-health/carbohydrate-digestion-and-absorption.

Luke, Hadyn. "The Importance of Fitness Testing." *CMS Fitness Courses*, 15 Jan. 2022, www.cmsfitnesscourses.co.uk/blog/the-importance-of-fitness-testing/.

Mahaffey, Kinsey. "Resistance Training Exercises & Concepts You Should Use." *NASM*, blog.nasm.org/resistance-training.

Maier, Anna, et al. "The Association between Test Anxiety, Self-Efficacy, and Mental Images among University Students: Results from an Online Survey." *Frontiers*, 30 Nov. 2021, www.frontiersin.org/articles/10.3389/fpsyt.2021.618108/full.

Miller, Ken. "Speed, Agility and Quickness: SAQ for You." *NASM*, 2021, blog.nasm.org/sports-performance/speed-agility-quickness-saq.

"Muscle Biomechanics." *Physiopedia*, www.physio-pedia.com/Muscle_Biomechanics.

NASM. "A Guide to the NASM Optimum Performance Training Model." *Premier Global*, 1 June 2020, blog.premierglobal.co.uk/a-guide-to-the-nasm-opt-model.

NASM. "CPT Exam Study Guide." *NASM*, www.nasm.org/docs/pdf/cpt7_study_guide.pdf?sfvrsn=1e28b0b_4.

NASM. "NASM Code of Professional Conduct." *NASM*, www.nasm.org/default-source/PDF/nasm-code-of-professional-conduct.pdf?sfvrsn=2.

NASM. "The Optimum Performance Training Model." *NASM*, ww.nasm.org/certified-personal-trainer/the-opt-model.

"NASM Practice Test." *Mometrix*, www.mometrix.com/academy/nasm-practice-test/.

National Cancer Institute. "Body Functions & Life Process." *NIH*, 2019, training.seer.cancer.gov/anatomy/body/functions.html.

National Cancer Institute. "Introduction to the Digestive System." *NIH*, 2019, training.seer.cancer.gov/anatomy/digestive/.

National Cancer Institute. "Introduction to the Endocrine System." *NIH*, 2020, training.seer.cancer.gov/anatomy/endocrine/.

National Cancer Institute. "Introduction to the Muscular System." *NIH*, 2019, training.seer.cancer.gov/anatomy/muscular/.

National Cancer Institute. "Introduction to the Nervous System." *NIH*, 2019, training.seer.cancer.gov/anatomy/nervous/.

National Cancer Institute. "Introduction to the Skeletal System." *NIH*, 2019, training.seer.cancer.gov/anatomy/skeletal/.

National Institute of Diabetes and Digestive and Kidney Diseases. "Your Digestive System & How It Works." *NIH*, 11 May 2023, www.niddk.nih.gov/health-information/digestive-diseases/digestive-system-how-it-works.

National Institutes of Health. "What Are the Parts of the Nervous System?" *NIH*, 2018, www.nichd.nih.gov/health/topics/neuro/conditioninfo/parts.

"Plyometric Training Concepts." *Fitness Mentors*, 25 July 2023, www.fitness-mentors.com/free-study-guide-for-the-nasm-cpt-exam-chapter-11-plyometric-training-concepts/.

PT Direct. "Muscle Roles and Contraction Types." *PT Direct*, 2010, www.ptdirect.com/training-design/anatomy-and-physiology/skeletal-muscle-roles-and-contraction-types.

Rad, Adrian. "Types of Movements in the Human Body." *Kenhub*, 20 July 2023, www.kenhub.com/en/library/anatomy/types-of-movements-in-the-human-body.

Read, Tyler. "NASM 6th Edition Chapter 8 - Cardiorespiratory Fitness Training." *Ptpioneer*, 22 Sept. 2023, www.ptpioneer.com/nasm-6th-edition-chapter-8/.

Read, Tyler. "NASM 6th Edition Chapter 11 - Plyometric Training Concepts." *Ptpioneer*, 22 Sept. 2023, www.ptpioneer.com/nasm-6th-edition-chapter-11/.

Read, Tyler. "NASM CPT 7th Edition Chapter 4: Behavioral Coaching." *Ptpioneer*, 22 Sept. 2023, www.ptpioneer.com/nasm-cpt-7th-edition-chapter-4/.

Read, Tyler. "NASM CPT 7th Edition Chapter 5: The Nervous, Skeletal, and Muscular Systems." *Ptpioneer*, 22 Sept. 2023, www.ptpioneer.com/nasm-cpt-7th-edition-chapter-5/.

Read, Tyler. "NASM CPT 7th Edition Chapter 6: The Cardiorespiratory, Endocrine, and Digestive Systems." *Www.ptpioneer.com*, 22 Sept. 2023, www.ptpioneer.com/nasm-cpt-7th-edition-chapter-6/.

Read, Tyler. "NASM CPT 7th Edition Chapter 15: Cardiorespiratory Training Concepts." *Ptpioneer*, 22 Sept. 2023, www.ptpioneer.com/nasm-cpt-7th-edition-chapter-15/.

Read, Tyler. "NASM CPT 7th Edition Chapter 17: Balance Training Concepts." *Ptpioneer*, 22 Sept. 2023, www.ptpioneer.com/nasm-cpt-7th-edition-chapter-17/.

Read, Tyler. "NASM CPT 7th Edition Chapter 18: Plyometric (Reactive) Training Concepts." *Ptpioneer*, 22 Sept. 2023, www.ptpioneer.com/nasm-cpt-7th-edition-chapter-18/.

Read, Tyler. "NASM CPT 7th Edition Chapter 20: Resistance Training Concepts." *Ptpioneer*, 22 Sept. 2023, www.ptpioneer.com/nasm-cpt-7th-edition-chapter-20/.

Read, Tyler. "NASM CPT 7th Edition Chapter 21: The Optimum Performance Training Model." *Ptpioneer*, 22 Sept. 2023, www.ptpioneer.com/nasm-cpt-7th-edition-chapter-21/.

Read, Tyler. "NASM CPT 7th Edition Chapter 22: Introduction to Exercise Modalities." *Ptpioneer*, 22 Sept. 2023, www.ptpioneer.com/nasm-cpt-7th-edition-chapter-22/.

Read, Tyler. "Study the NASM CPT 7th Edition Chapter 19: Speed, Agility, and Quickness Training Concepts. Learn to Coach SAQ Training & Pass Your NASM CNC Exam." *Ptpioneer*, 22 Sept. 2023, www.ptpioneer.com/nasm-cpt-7th-edition-chapter-19/.

Read, Tyler. "NASM CPT 7th Edition Chapter 2: The Personal Training Profession." *Ptpioneer*, 22 Sept. 2023, www.ptpioneer.com/nasm-cpt-7th-edition-chapter-2/.

Read, Tyler. "NASM CPT 7th Edition Chapter 3: Psychology of Exercise." *Ptpioneer*, 22 Sept. 2023, www.ptpioneer.com/nasm-cpt-7th-edition-chapter-3/.

Read, Tyler. "NASM CPT 7th Edition Chapter 8: Exercise Metabolism and Bioenergetics." *Ptpioneer*, 22 Sept. 2023, www.ptpioneer.com/nasm-cpt-7th-edition-chapter-8/.

Read, Tyler. "NASM CPT 7th Edition Chapter 10: Supplementation." *Ptpioneer*, 22 Sept. 2023, www.ptpioneer.com/nasm-cpt-7th-edition-chapter-10/.

Read, Tyler. "NASM CPT 7th Edition Chapter 11: Health, Wellness, and Fitness Assessments." *Ptpioneer*, 22 Sept. 2023, www.ptpioneer.com/nasm-cpt-7th-edition-chapter-11/.

Read, Tyler. "NASM CPT 7th Edition Chapter 13: Integrated Training and the OPT Model." *Ptpioneer*, 22 Sept. 2023, www.ptpioneer.com/nasm-cpt-7th-edition-chapter-13/.

Read, Tyler. "NASM CPT 7th Edition Chapter 16: Core Training Concepts." *Ptpioneer*, 22 Sept. 2023, www.ptpioneer.com/nasm-cpt-7th-edition-chapter-16/.

Read, Tyler. "NASM CPT 7th Edition Chapter 1: The Modern State of Health and Fitness." *Ptpioneer*, 22 Sept. 2023, www.ptpioneer.com/nasm-cpt-7th-edition-chapter-1/.

Read, Tyler. "NASM CPT 7th Edition Chapter 9: Nutrition." *Ptpioneer*, 22 Sept. 2023, www.ptpioneer.com/nasm-cpt-7th-edition-chapter-9/.

Read, Tyler. "NASM CPT 7th Edition Chapter 12: Posture, Movement, and Performance Assessments." *Ptpioneer*, 22 Sept. 2023, www.ptpioneer.com/nasm-cpt-7th-edition-chapter-12/.

Read, Tyler. "NASM CPT 7th Edition Chapter 14: Flexibility Training Concepts." *Ptpioneer*, 22 Sept. 2023, www.ptpioneer.com/nasm-cpt-7th-edition-chapter-14/.

Read, Tyler. "NASM CPT 7th Edition Chapter 23: Chronic Health Conditions and Special Populations." *Ptpioneer*, 22 Sept. 2023, www.ptpioneer.com/nasm-cpt-7th-edition-chapter-23/.

Read, Tyler. "NASM CPT 7th Edition Chapter 7: Human Movement Science." *Www.ptpioneer.com*, 22 Sept. 2023, www.ptpioneer.com/nasm-cpt-7th-edition-chapter-7/.

Sahrmann, Shirley A. "The Human Movement System: Our Professional Identity." *Physical Therapy*, vol. 94, no. 7, 1 July 2014, pp. 1034–1042, https://doi.org/10.2522/ptj.20130319.

Sawchuck, Craig. "Test Anxiety: Can It Be Treated?" *Mayo Clinic*, 3 Aug. 2017, www.mayoclinic.org/diseases-conditions/generalized-anxiety-disorder/expert-answers/test-anxiety/faq-20058195.

Sutton, Brian. "A Practical Approach to Training the Muscle Synergies." *NASM*, blog.nasm.org/ces/practical-approach-training-muscle-synergies.

Sutton, Brian . "An Explanation of the New Updates to the OPT Model." *NASM*, blog.nasm.org/new-opt-model-updates.

Swaim, Emily. "8 Tips to Calm Test Anxiety so You Can Test Your Best." *Healthline*, 9 Mar. 2022, www.healthline.com/health/how-to-overcome-test-anxiety.

"Test Anxiety Tips." *Loma Linda University School of Medicine*, medicine.llu.edu/academics/resources/test-anxiety-tips.

United States Environmental Protection Agency. "Overview of the Endocrine System." *EPA*, 6 July 2015, www.epa.gov/endocrine-disruption/overview-endocrine-system.

Made in United States
North Haven, CT
02 May 2024

52018842R00122